The story of the

Kerry Bog Pony

MARY MCGRATH & GAY KEOGH

Æ

ASSOCIATED EDITIONS

The Story of the Kerry Bog Pony

Published in 2010 by Associated Editions,
33 Melrose Avenue, Fairview, Dublin 3, Ireland
www.associatededitions.ie

Book design by Vermillion Design, Dublin.

Photography © Rae Brocklehurst, Leo Curran,
Michael Diggin, Aisling Heffernan, Gay Keogh,
Joseph Keogh, Pascal Lando, Don MacMonagle,
Mary McGrath, John Mulvihill, Valerie O'Sullivan,
PD's Photos, Emmanuelle Poiret, David Shaw Smith.
Every effort has been made by the authors to
acknowledge correct copyright of images where
applicable. Any errors or omissions are unintentional.

A CIP record for this title is available from the
British Library

ISBN 978-1-906429-12-6

For John and Olive

Thank you

The Department of Agriculture, Fisheries and Food's Grant Aid Scheme for the Conservation of Genetic Resources for Food and Agriculture whose funding made possible the publication of this book. Helen Mulligan, Mark Maguire in the Department of Agriculture, Fisheries and Food; John and Olive Mulvihill and family and all at the Red Fox Inn for suitcases full of information and for wonderful hospitality; Michael Teahan Snr, Michael Teahan Jnr, Tom Moriarty and Mossie Pierce for all their help and good humour, Dr Leo Curran and Mary Curran for steadfast support and encouragement, Thanks also to Michele Desmond, Castlecove, Co Kerry and Eugene McGovern, Omagh, Co Tyrone, for sending me valuable information, Pat and Sinead Byrne for their support and knowledge of the Studbook; Aoife Leach at Adams Art Auctions, Seamus MacPhilib at the National Museum of Country Life, Patricia Moloney, Librarian, and Johnny Dillon, Archivist, at the National Folklore Collection, UCD, Gerard Whelan, Librarian at the Royal Dublin Society, Marita Corcoran, Local Studies Department, Kerry County Council, Eamonn Kelly, National Museum of Ireland and Jenny Murray at the Shetland Museum, all of whom assisted us in accessing their archives; Norah Byrne and Donna Craig at Horse Sport Ireland; Ilona Blunden and Niamh Carey for help with the manuscript; to Annie West for generously providing the illustration "What if......". Don Conroy, David White, Teddy Clifford MRCVS, Dr Stuart Lane, Raimonde Hilliard, Clare Hoare, Mary Tarry, J.P. McCarthy at *The Kerryman*, Paddy McMonagle, Tucks Bergin, Denis Garvey, Ben Hussey, Maria Bennett and Con Keogh, and to others too numerous to mention individually who provided information and help. To Joseph Keogh for his unfailing enthusiasm and support. Finally we would like to thank Patricia McGrath without whom we would not have been possible!

Special thanks

To our specialist contributors: Dr John Flynn and Aisling Heffernan, Weatherbys DNA Laboratory, Dr John Feehan, Faculty of Agriculture at UCD, Dr. David Shaw-Smith, Documentary Film Maker, Paddy Mathews, Environment and Planning, Fáilte Ireland and Una Cosgrove, Heritage Officer, Kerry County Council: and to Dr Leo Curran who kindly agreed to provide the foreword for this book.

Particular thanks to Michael Diggin for his great photographs, enthusiasm and support.

Photo © Pascal Lando

CONTENTS

FOREWORD

High amongst the rugged beauty of the Kerry Mountains there is an area known as *Com na gCapall* – Recess of the Horses. Towering above it is *Cathair na bhFéinne* – Dwelling Place of the Fianna. Each forms part of *Na Cruacha Dubha* – The Black Reeks that are more generally known today as The MacGillacuddy Reeks. A romantic element in my Celtic imagination would like to infer that such ancient place names stem from real connections to events of the past, but that is quite unlikely. Ireland's oral tradition of myth and legend, including that relating to chariots and horses, seems to have been very creative and inventive long before the skills of writing were introduced and long before vellum and ink became available.

An example of such imagery is conveyed by the Irish proverb: *Is minic a dhèanann bromachín giobalach capaillín cumasach"* – a rough looking colt often becomes a good-looking pony. Such sentiments summarise the far-sighted view taken by John Mulvihill of Glenbeigh when, in 1990, he identified a need to rescue from extinction the small working pony of the Kerry countryside. John has a deep love of Kerry and its people and is much involved in community endeavours. Our paths crossed in 1992 when John Whyte of Sneem told me about the Mulvihill pony conservation effort. I was in Sneem to deliver a lecture on the history and conservation of the breed of Kerry Cattle. The event formed part of the Extension Lecture Series promoted by the Royal Dublin Society and resulted from publication of my book: *Kerry and Dexter Cattle: A History.* On the following day I travelled to *The Red Fox Inn* for my first encounter with John Mulvihill and his ponies. An enduring bond of friendship was established with the Mulvihill family. Two years later I assisted with the establishment of *The Irish Genetic Resources Conservation Trust Limited* and John Mulvihill came to an early meeting of the Trust in Trinity College Dublin where he spoke enthusiastically about the urgent need to conserve *The Kerry Bog Pony.* He was urged to record details of each pony and its offspring so as to form a sound breeding-base for the herd.

At that stage John had the assistance of a small and enthusiastic committee the members of which confirmed a breed description including endorsement of the name chosen by John. He and his fellow committee members were

unaware at that time of an attempt made in 1973 by others in Kerry to conserve what they called *The Kerry Pony.* That earlier approach seems to have been focused on the performance of small Kerry ponies at local and county shows, rather than focused on conservation of a foundation breeding stock. However, that Society's work crumbled and the pony population which it had sought to promote went into decline. A significant part of that decline was evident on the Kerry landscape where the traditional small working ponies on family farms became less evident as a heritage component of rural life.

Small tractors became a more convenient power-source to bring turf home from the bog and there was no longer a perceived use for the small ponies. Nevertheless, John Mulvihill was not deterred in his conservation attempt. A presence of Kerry Bog Ponies on the rugged landscape formed part of a tradition that could connect visiting tourists with a very different past. He bought as many of these heritage animals as he could find and from a collection of 20 mares and six stallions he developed his own mental image of the typical conformation that was representative of the breed. He got much sustained support from local representatives of the veterinary profession. One of those, Timothy Clifford M.R.C.V.S., became a member of the first committee and assisted with the formulation of a clear conservation objective for the Kerry Bog Pony. Once a foundation was created for future progress the Society became an incorporated body, *The Kerry Bog Pony Co-operative Society Limited* in 2005. It enjoys great support from Ireland's Department of Agriculture,Fisheries and Food, from Horse Sport Ireland and from a variety of other bodies such as Weatherbys Ireland and The Irish Cattle Breeding Federation.

I take this opportunity to wish the Co-op a very bright future and to thank my good friend, Mary McGrath, for her intensive searches for clues about the ponies from a literature that provides scant evidence.

Leo Curran

2010

INTRODUCTION

Mary McGrath

We grew up surrounded by horses – all sorts of horses: thoroughbreds, showjumpers, hunters and ponies. Our Dad loved horses and when he stopped hunting he returned to driving where he had left off during the war. He drove a Hackney then a Welsh Cob but finally settled for a pair and then a team of Irish Draughts. As children we rode Connemara Ponies and grew to value the attributes of Native Breeds. They were hardy and kind, intelligent and easy to work with. So when I heard on the radio that John Mulvihill of the Red Fox Inn had rediscovered an old Irish Breed of pony I was very interested. Then at the Kildare County Show I saw an exhibit of a beautiful little stallion labelled "Kerry Bog Pony". It was Quagmire Prince.

I went to Glenbeigh to see John Mulvihill's ponies "of the old breed". I asked him if he had two matching ponies and he rounded up two little bay youngsters with white points. They were both out of a lovely mare called

Mary and young passengers driving the pair of ponies, Bog Birch and Boggy Boy, at the National Show in Glenbeigh

Birch Bog Lady and by Flashy Fox, John's foundation stallion. I fell for them straight away and brought them home with me.

Their personality is totally different to the other two native breeds - the Connemara and the Irish Draught. These ponies have a sense of fun. They play like puppies when they are first let out, chasing one another in circles, bucking and squealing. They race the car and horsebox as I drive along the avenue. They come running when they are called. They are like terriers in that they don't know they are small. They are brave, strong, have big hearts and are as cute as foxes. They are now broken to harness (more or less) and have made my life a lot more exciting of late.

"A job shared is a job halved"

To date we have no records as to how the ponies arrived in this part of Kerry. Genetic evidence shows that the ponies originated in Northwest Europe. Could they have come in with the Vikings? There was a Viking settlement on Beginish Island and other settlements around Dingle Bay in the 9th and 10th centuries. But why do similar ponies not show up in other Viking settlement areas dotted all along the western coastline? What is it about this part of Kerry that preserved this unique pony?

Before studbooks were introduced in Ireland in the late 18th and early 19th centuries animal breeds were described by type. Regional pony types evolved to suit local requirements. At one period there were the Erris Pony, the Roscommon Pony, the Donegal Pony, the Rathlin Pony, the Cushendall Pony and many others which are now all extinct. In the 1880s there were six very different types of Connemara Pony which have now been selectively bred into one breed in a single studbook.

Kerry and other parts of the west were geographically and therefore socially isolated before the advent of a road network. We rely on government surveys and travellers' diaries for snippets of relevant information but Kerry Bog Ponies never seem to have existed in large numbers and mentions are few and far between. Images are almost non-existent. No breeding records were kept. If we did not have the ponies on the ground it would be very hard to prove that they ever existed. This makes their survival even more remarkable.

This is not a history book nor is it a text book. It tells the story of the Kerry Bog Pony today and how the breed was saved from extinction. We have invited a number of experts to write about their specialist subjects and photographer Michael Diggin has supplied many beautiful photographs.

I must mention here the amazing national collections available to researchers in this country, the enthusiasm of those who care for them and the generosity with which they share their knowledge.

This book celebrates the Kerry Bog Pony in its traditional context. This includes its historical uses as a draught animal, its importance to small family enterprises and its changing role over the centuries. In this way history, commerce, nature, botany, crafts, traditional knowledge and modern science based practices are all shown to play important interlinked roles.

The Kerry Bog Pony conservation project has local, national and international significance. It is the story of the Kerry Bog Pony's survival as a distinct breed in spite of all the odds. From near extinction in 1992 when only 6 stallions and 20 mares were known to survive, to today's population of almost 400 ponies, the current success story is the result of one man's vision helped by local farmers whose crucial role as custodians of the breed is acknowledged. The voluntary efforts of a concerned group of conservationists

Ponies performing a traditional task on the bog

Ceol agus Craic at the Red Fox Inn

aided at every step of the way by official resources are also noted. We would like to mention here the legendary hospitality extended to all by John, Olive and Tim Mulvihill at the Red Fox Inn.

The steps undertaken to preserve the Kerry Bog Pony are outlined so that increased awareness will enhance the understanding of effective approaches to the conservation of genetic biodiversity. Increased publicity will instil pride in a local product while confirming the importance attached to maintaining a rare breed by the national authorities. The Kerry Bog Pony is an important addition to Ireland's biodiversity and has a European significance way beyond its actual herd numbers.

We have tried to tell the story as it happened. We are sorry if people feel they have been left out but records are scarce from the early days of the Society. Many people have played very important roles in ensuring the survival of the Kerry Bog Pony – especially the breeders. It is thanks to them that the Kerry Bog Pony survives today.

THE KERRY BOG PONY TODAY

Mary McGrath & Gay Keogh

The Kerry Bog Pony is a small, sturdy, working pony. Standing at around 11 hands high, it is extremely strong for its size and generally weighs around 200 kilos or 4 cwts.

ORIGINAL DISTRIBUTION

Kerry Bog Pony Stallions have great presence and good temperaments

While little is known of the exact origins of the Kerry Bog Pony, the adjoining map shows their known distribution, based on historical records. Nowadays, while their numbers are low, they are to be found in many counties throughout Ireland.

BREED DESCRIPTION

The Kerry Bog Pony has a fine, intelligent head with large kind eyes. It has a strong and well set on neck, with a rounded shoulder and compact body. It generally has a long flowing mane and tail. In its native county, rainfall is extremely high. In its natural state the pony's mane often splits to fall either side of the neck deflecting the rain as it falls. The pony is clean legged with very little feather to its heels. It has good bone, with short cannon bones, short pasterns and upright hooves. It comes in a variety of whole colours, with chestnut and bays the most common.

The Kerry Bog Pony is extremely hardy, resistant to many equine diseases, with great powers of endurance. It has ample bone, and can carry heavy burdens in relation to its build. Traditionally it would have been used as a pack animal carrying heavy loads.

Tralee
Killorglin
Dingle   Killarney
Mangerton
Mountain
Valentia Island   Kenmare

Left: Kerry is located on the Atlantic seaboard in the south-west of Ireland. The historical range of the Kerry Bog Pony seems to have been confined to the south Kerry area.

Below: The Ponies come in a variety of whole colours

Pony trotting on rough ground showing its natural elevation

Opposite: Mares working on the bog were often accompanied by their foals. Photo © Michael Diggin

ACTION

Its action is straight with good elevation. In common with other native breeds this type of action was needed to navigate rough and rocky ground. It is very sure-footed and has strong legs and feet with a smooth stride.

The Kerry Bog Pony has a definite identity and appearance of its own. Type is the most important factor and the hardest to define. Kerry Bog Ponies do not look like Shetland Ponies or Welsh Ponies. Specific characteristics have been identified and average measurements have been compiled from a representative sample of ponies to create the Phenotype.

BREED STANDARD

The characteristics of the Kerry Bog Pony (KBP) are as originally defined in 1994 and as re-affirmed unanimously as the Breed Standard at the First AGM of the Kerry Bog Pony Co-operative Society held on 26th February 2005. They are as follows:

Size: This is a small pony evolved as such because of its use as a draught animal in the bogs of Kerry over the centuries. Thus, the height of the Kerry Bog pony is 102cms – 117cms for Stallions and Geldings and 102cms – 112cms for Mares.

Colour: Any strong whole colour is to be found but colour is generally brown or brownish black and bay. Some chestnut, grey and dun colours are also to be found.

Coat: The coat of the KBP is long and dense and easily capable of withstanding harsh winter conditions without shelter.

Head: The head is pleasant, plain and of average size and rather dish-faced. Ears are small and pointed. Nostrils allow large air intake relative to body size. The jaw is strong and well formed with excellent dentition to facilitate grazing on heath, gorse and heather.

Body: The neck is strong and medium length. The shoulder is rounded and muscular. The body is strong and compact. The chest is deep with well-sprung ribs and good girth. Loins are powerful and the hindquarters are strong and well-formed. The tail is full, abundant and well set and well carried.

A sample of ponies were measured to create a phenotype for the breed

PHENOTYPIC CHARACTERISTICS

Phenotype = The characteristics of an organism, as determined by both genetic makeup and environmental influences

Trait Number	Trait Description	Range (cm)	Average measurement (cm)
1	Distance between eyes	14-17.5	16
2	Length of Ears	12-16	14
3	Muzzle circumference	33-46	38
4	Throat width	3-8	5
5	Head-neck circumference	33-46	38
6	Forearm length	29-37	34
7	Knee circumference	18-28	24
8	Front cannon length	18-23.5	21
9	Front cannon circumference	14-17.5	16
10	Front pastern length	6-9	7
11	Shoulder length	50-67	58
12	Chest width	18-32	25
13	Back length	77-99	86
14	Girth circumference	123-170	148
15	Hind cannon length	30-36	31
16	Hind cannon circumference	16-29	16
17	Hind pastern length	6-9	7
18	Distance between hips	38-58	48

POINTS OF THE PONY

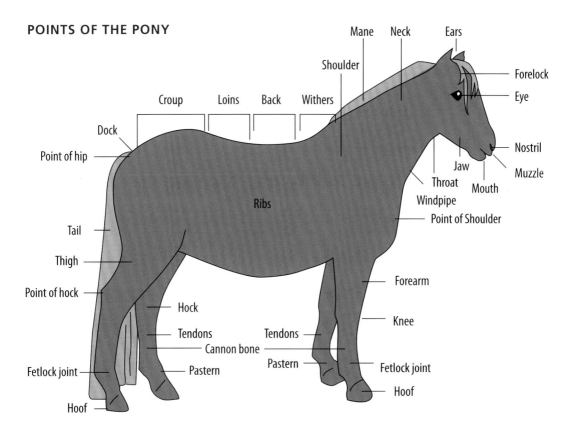

Legs: The forelegs are strong and muscular with a strong forearm. Hind legs are muscular and powerful. The cannon bone is short with flat hard bone of good size. Pasterns are short and the hooves upright, wide open and well formed of hard horn requiring very little trimming.

Action: The KBP is a powerful pony with good bone and great weight and strength relative to its size. This, together with its excellent conformation, gives the pony a lovely straight and level action with good balance. This intelligent pony is sure footed and well capable of thinking for itself in the soft underfoot conditions of Kerry bogs.

Temperament and Character: This pony, while kind, sensible, confident and well mannered, also possesses great courage and endurance. Viciousness or nervousness have been bred out of the KBP at a much earlier stage. Soundness is also a feature of the KBP; hereditary unsoundness is extremely rare and because of the pony's innate strength and toughness it scarcely ever develops any unsoundness. The animal's constitution is also first class, being possessed of large heart and lung room which in turn enables it to thrive well in spite of harsh weather or other difficulties. The excellent temperament of the pony allows it to be easily trained to harness or saddle and it can be easily worked as a children's riding pony (Source: Timothy G. Clifford, MVB, MRCVS).

WEIGHT OF KERRY BOG PONY

This is to certify that the average bodyweight of a Kerry Bog Pony is of the order of 190-220kg.

This is based on weighings carried out on a number of Kerry Bog Ponies on 7/12/95 at Leslie West's Weighing Scales, Anglont, Killorglin on behalf of John Mulvihill of the Kerry Bog Village.

T.G. Clifford MVB, MRCVS, Prendiville, Mangan & Clifford, Veterinary Surgeons, Upper Bridge St, Killorglin, County Kerry

Given shelter and fodder ponies are happy to out-winter even in snow

REGISTRATION

The Kerry Bog Pony Studbook of Origin is held by the Kerry Bog Pony Co-operative Society under licence from the Department of Agriculture, Fisheries and Food. The Register is maintained by Horse Sport Ireland. Every pony born to Kerry Bog Pony parents is entitled to be in the Register. All foals enter the Register as Class 4. At two years old and over ponies can be inspected at which time they will be classified as Class 1, 2 or 3 depending on their results. (For details of the Inspection procedures please see Chapter 6 – Inspections & Shows).

CLASSIFICATION

There are 4 classes in the *Kerry Bog Pony Studbook*.

Class 1 conforms exactly to the Breed Standard as regards height, etc.

Class 2 is for ponies that are either too big or too small but which otherwise conform to the Breed Standard.

Class 3 is for ponies that fail inspection on grounds of unsoundness, colour, temperament, etc.

Class 4 is for uninspected ponies.

The offspring of uninspected (Class 4) ponies are not eligible for classification in the Studbook. The offspring of Classes 1, 2 and 3 are eligible for inspection and classification.

BREED PURPOSE

The Kerry Bog Pony is a multi-purpose breed. It is bred to work and can pull a laden cart or carry creels of turf or seaweed as it did in times gone by.

It can be used by children as a riding pony or as a driving pony by adults. They are classified as a Mountain and Moorland breed. At present there are very few show classes for Kerry Bog Ponies but hopefully more will come on stream as their numbers increase.

Showing: Traditionally Mountain and Moorland ponies are shown in their "native" state and are not trimmed or plaited. In reality a little light trimming is commonplace, for example to show off a fine head ponies often have their manes pulled to a tidy length and laid on the off side. In some cases, trimming

Correct show class turnout for pony and handler

is necessary, for example if a pony's tail was left to grow unchecked it could become matted or trail along the ground. Their feet should be dressed but do not need to be shod unless they are doing roadwork.

In Hand: When shown in hand, young stock are shown in a headcollar, preferably leather, while older animals can be shown in a snaffle bit and led from a leather coupling. Fancy browbands are not suitable for the show ring. Handlers should be dressed neatly, wearing appropriate footwear as you will be expected to run with your pony. A show cane can be carried.

Riding: In ridden classes a shirt and tie is traditionally worn with a tweed jacket, gloves, cream jodhpurs and jodhpur boots. An approved riding hat must be worn. The bridle should be plain and workmanlike. A straight cut or working hunter saddle is best to show off the pony's shoulder and action. All tack should be clean and well fitting.

Driving: Driving classes are a specialised area with different types of attire, harness and vehicle for different disciplines: showing, cross country, dressage etc. Advice should be sought from an experienced source about the appropriate turnout for horse and driver. Once again all harness must be in good condition,

Left: A smart driving turnout

Below: The ponies are very versatile and children can enjoy using them in a variety of disciplines

25

clean and well fitting. Safety rules should be followed at all times e.g. if giving the pony a drink the bridle should never be removed while the pony is still harnessed to the vehicle. (This may seem obvious but this is one of the most common mistakes made by the inexperienced at driving competitions).

QUESTIONS TO ASK BEFORE PURCHASING A KERRY BOG PONY:

What will it be used for? The pony should be suitable for its purpose.

- A stallion would not be suitable for a small child to ride.
- Geldings are very versatile and suitable for most disciplines.
- Native breeds are slow to mature, so young ponies should not be overworked.

If you want to breed Kerry Bog Ponies a suitable mare should be chosen.

- How do I select a suitable mare?
- A suitable mare for breeding should be at least 3 years of age and well handled.
- She must be registered, microchipped and have a "Brown Passport".
- She should be inspected and classified, as offspring from unclassified ponies are not eligible to be inspected for classification.

BREEDING THE KERRY BOG PONY

A Kerry Bog Pony foal trotting

The Kerry Bog Pony is classified as a "local breed in danger of extinction". Therefore, if you intend to breed your mare there are a lot of issues to consider. Firstly, make sure your mare's paperwork is in order and that she is registered in your name, so that there will be no problems when you come to register your foal.

Choosing the best stallion for your mare is very important as numbers are very low. With less than 200 mares and 36 Class 1 stallions from 16 bloodlines, it is essential that a close eye be kept on the pedigrees to avoid breeding animals that might be closely related. Inbreeding can increase the possibility of defects and infertility. In 2007, at the request of the Department of Agriculture, Fisheries and Food, the Cattle Breeders Federation carried out

an analysis of the bloodlines of all the registered animals using their specialised computer software. They then advised owners of the most suitable stallions for their mare. Of course, once the pedigree is suitable you must also ensure that the stallion suits your mare and perhaps improves the offspring. For instance, if your mare is slightly weak in the quarters, using a powerful wellbuilt stallion could produce a more balanced foal. Beware of using a stallion with a "bad" head and "good" quarters on your mare that has a "good" head and "bad" quarters – it's quite possible that you could end up with a pony with a "bad head and bad quarters"! The use of Class 1 stallions is advised as the best way to achieve a good-looking foal.

Foals are best left with the mare for 6 months before weaning

It is also important to plan when you want your foal to be born. The gestation period for a pony is eleven months. The most suitable foaling time is usually around April, May or June, as at this time there is plenty of grass and the weather should be warm. So your choice of stallion should be made early in the year.

When your mare is in season, take her to your chosen stallion. Bring your mare's passport and ensure that you get a Covering Certificate from the stallion owner before taking the mare home.

Select a stallion that suits your mare taking account of conformation and pedigree. Photo © Pascal Lando

The stallion owner also returns a copy of the Covering Certificate to Horse Sport Ireland. The following year when the foal is born, you will receive a Kit containing a marking chart and the requirements for DNA sampling. This must be carried out by a veterinary surgeon. Full instructions are given for these procedures and on completion you will receive a Class 4 passport for your foal. In Ireland it is a legal requirement that every equine (horses, ponies and donkeys) must be microchipped and have a passport.

WELFARE

Although Kerry Bog Ponies are a hardy native breed, good standards of care are still essential for their welfare. You should have regular visits from your farrier, have your pony's teeth checked and carry out routine worming. When grazing

Getting down to
the job!

on their native surroundings the ponies are not prone to heavy worm
infestations, however, every situation is different and you should consult your
veterinary surgeon as to the quantity and frequency of dosing. The ponies are
very "good doers" – they need relatively little food to live on. Care should be
taken not to allow overgrazing on lush pasture as they can become overweight
and develop health problems, including laminitis. However, sufficient pasture
to allow rotation of grazing is necessary to minimise worm infestation. Like all
equines, these ponies are herd animals and appreciate being kept in company.

The Kerry Bog Pony has a great temperament - the result of generations
of use on small farms. Ponies were selected for their ability to work calmly
and well in a variety of different roles. When handled kindly the Kerry Bog
Pony is quick to learn and willing to please.

GENETIC ASPECTS OF THE KERRY BOG PONY

John Flynn, Aisling Heffernan

While there is very little documentation to explain their existence, science has shown us that the Kerry Bog Pony is a distinct breed which is now characterised at genetic level. Dr John Flynn MSc, FIMLS, Scientific Director of Weatherbys DNA Laboratory, Irish Equine Centre, Johnstown, Kill, Co. Kildare and Aisling Heffernan MSc, also of Weatherbys DNA Laboratory, carried out a programme of genetic testing which began in 1994 as blood typing. In 1998 in accordance with the international scientific body "The International Society for Animal Genetics" (ISAG) the laboratory changed from blood typing to DNA genotyping. Since then all Kerry Bog Pony stallions, brood mares and offspring are DNA typed prior to registration.

Perhaps it is due to the physical geography of Kerry that the pony survived

Within the animal kingdom the equine species (*Equus caballus*) forms a hierarchical population consisting of sub-populations of many different breeds which are dispersed throughout the world. Some equine breeds are considered native to a particular country, while other breeds migrated to or were imported from other parts of the world. Down through the centuries many equine sub-populations were formed as a result of confinement to particular regions due to geographical boundaries or by migrating to regions that were adaptable due to climatic conditions and pasture availability.

In terms of the domesticated horse, Ireland, the Scottish Highlands and the North Atlantic islands can be viewed as separate cultural and geographical locations. These regions are characterised by the prevalence of hardy, sure-footed ponies that survived in harsh landscapes with little care.

Pony breeds generally evolved in harsh climates with scant vegetation resulting in a dwarfing effect on animal size and measuring less than 148cm at the withers when fully mature. As a result of their hardy nature and often quiet disposition in conjunction with their low maintenance costs, requiring less feeding and shelter, ponies were frequently used to carry out work on farms and in industry instead of horses. The Kerry Bog Pony would be a typical example of the evolution of one such equine breed. With specific characteristics such as its small stature and soundness of limb it adapted to working in bog lands and transporting peat throughout the south-west region of Ireland.

Ponies thrive under a variety of conditions as the breed has adapted to its environs

Historically peat was the main source of domestic energy for local communities. For centuries, humans relied heavily on the use of horses and ponies as a source of horse-power in industry, agriculture and transport. However, since the end of the 19th century, through the mechanisation of farming practices and transport and the development of new technologies in industry, our daily lives have become increasingly less dependent on the use of these animals. Although these developments have led to an arguably more convenient and comfortable existence for humans they have resulted in a severe reduction in number within many native horse and pony breeds. This gradual reduction in population numbers is called genetic erosion. The Kerry Bog Pony is an example of an equine population that underwent severe reduction in numbers which eventually led to it becoming an endangered species. This led to concern in local communities which inspired an initiative led by John Mulvihill to arrest this situation and embark upon a programme of conservation of the Kerry Bog Pony.

There are numerous biological, social and economical reasons as to why the conservation of animal genetic resources is so important. Biologically it is crucial because the genetic diversity contained within animal breeds is necessary for them to be able to adjust in response to environmental change. Since the only way to introduce new genetic diversity into breeds is through the extremely slow process of mutation it is vital that the maximum amount of diversity be preserved in populations while it is still possible to do so.

GENETIC CHARACTERISATION OF THE KERRY BOG PONY

Genetic characterisation is often the first step in any conservation plan. These studies usually involve one or more technologies that can identify heritable genetic markers within and between equine populations. In the past, red blood cell typing and biochemical protein polymorphisms were the only technologies available but their potential in population genetics was rather restricted due to the lack of genetic markers identified by these systems. However, more recently, with advanced technology, nuclear DNA (nDNA) analysis and/or mitochondrial (mtDNA) sequence variation analysis have become the obvious methods in genetic population studies.

DNA SAMPLING PROCEDURE

In order to obtain genetic information from DNA the procedure begins with the collection of hair samples with follicles from the mane or tail by a veterinary surgeon. These samples are placed in a small plastic bag, clearly labelled and sent to Weatherbys DNA Laboratory where they are processed.

KBP pony hairs in sample bags

Processing of KBP samples in Weatherbys DNA Laboratory

STEP 1: Each KBP is assigned a laboratory reference DNA number.

STEP 2: Six hairs from each sample with roots attached are placed in a small tube and cut.

STEP 3: DNA is extracted from the cut hairs

STEP 4: Polymerase Chain Reaction (PCR) is carried out on each sample of extracted DNA.

STEP 5: Each sample is then run on the genetic analyser.

STEP 6: The electropherograms are analysed and the results are sent to the database of all previously DNA typed horses. The results can then be used for parentage testing of each KBP.

A. Nuclear DNA is inherited from all ancestors

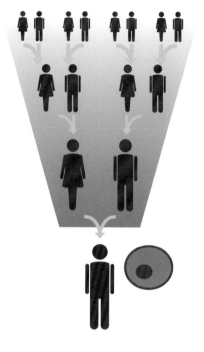

B. Mitochondrial DNA is inherited from a single lineage

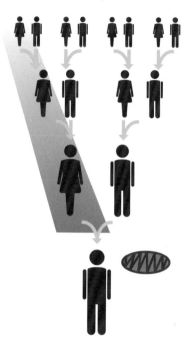

The nDNA analysis is based on the principle of DNA fragment analysis of non-coding, co-dominant and highly polymorphic repeat sequence motifs, which are called microsatellites. The number of repeats present at a particular locus represents the different alleles, the frequencies of which are used to calculate the statistical parameters required for the characterisation study. These statistical parameters can in turn provide information on the genetic diversity, relationships and origins of different breeds. mtDNA analysis involves examining the mitochondrial DNA sequence variation between individuals in a population.

In addition to advances in molecular cell biology, the last decade has seen unprecedented technological development in the field of computer software. Computer packages have been developed to assist humans in almost every aspect of our daily lives and molecular biology is no exception. With regard to population genetics, the arduous task of direct counting of detected alleles and the complicated mathematical computations involved in determining the necessary statistical parameters have all been replaced with computer programs designed to conduct the counting and calculation on our behalf. With these modern developments to assist them, population geneticists are now in a position to thoroughly investigate the genetic characteristics of countless species which will be of immense benefit for the conservation of these plants and animals.

There are a number of statistical parameters routinely determined during breed characterisation studies. The first and most fundamental component in a genetic diversity study utilises the Hardy-Weinberg Theory which involves the principle of observed and expected values of gene frequencies within a breed inherited from one generation to the next. A typical example of this would be the estimation of the parameters of observed and expected heterozygosities which are calculated from the allele frequencies identified at each genetic site, giving an indication of the level of inbreeding within a particular breed.

NUCLEAR DNA

In our study of the Kerry Bog Pony, we identified genetic markers at 17 different sites in 172 ponies. This constituted an excellent source of data to carry out genetic characterisation of this breed. The analysis of the nDNA microsatellites revealed large amounts of interesting genetic information about the KBP. We have now determined high levels of genetic variation and differentiation in the population. The high level of genetic variation in the KBP, despite the small population size, is most likely due to the varied background of a large number of the ponies tested during this investigation. The main founding population of the breed consisted of six stallions and 20 mares. These animals were selected due to their phenotypic traits alone as there was no pedigree information available. Although these foundation stock animals were of the correct 'type' of pony, in that they all exhibited the same desired phenotypic traits including conformation, abilities and character, it is likely that they had a very diverse genetic pool. We have also shown that the level of inbreeding is not currently a cause for concern and in spite of historical evidence of a genetic bottleneck due to a reduction in numbers, there was no evidence of this in our statistical analysis. This again suggests that our present population may be comprised of a diverse selection of ponies with similar phenotypic characteristics.

MITOCHONDRIAL DNA

In conjunction with this nDNA investigation, mitochondrial DNA sequence analysis was also carried out on 39 maternally unrelated ponies. By sequencing a highly variable region of the mitochondria, it was possible to detect mutations in the sequence. These different mutations are known as haplotypes. This part of the genetic characterisation study was designed to determine the possible geographical origins of the Kerry Bog Pony. The question of the origins of the KBP is of great interest to the scientific and non-scientific communities alike. The story of the rescue of this rare pony from almost certain extinction by a small dedicated group of people has raised much interest nationally and internationally. But up until now, the beginning of this story has always been obscured because we did not know the origins of the KBP.

HAPLOGROUPS

In order to begin to try and determine the geographical origins of the founding population of the KBP, the frequencies of mtDNA haplogroups found in the KBP population were compared to the haplogroup frequencies found in 68 other horse and pony populations throughout the world. Analysis

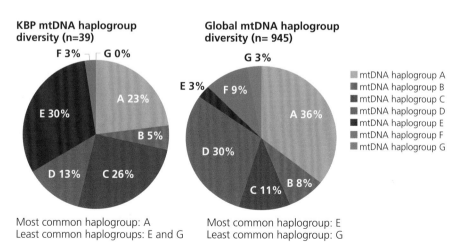

KBP mtDNA haplogroup diversity (n=39)

F 3%   G 0%
A 23%
E 30%
B 5%
D 13%   C 26%

Global mtDNA haplogroup diversity (n= 945)

G 3%
E 3%   F 9%
A 36%
D 30%
C 11%   B 8%

mtDNA haplogroup A
mtDNA haplogroup B
mtDNA haplogroup C
mtDNA haplogroup D
mtDNA haplogroup E
mtDNA haplogroup F
mtDNA haplogroup G

Most common haplogroup: A
Least common haplogroups: E and G

Most common haplogroup: E
Least common haplogroup: G

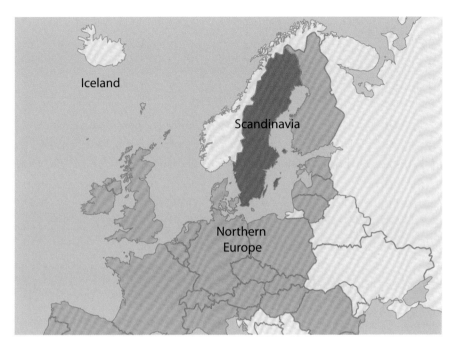

The genetic make-up of the Kerry Bog Pony is linked to pony breeds in the more Northern regions of Europe and Scandinavia

of the mtDNA sequence variation of the KBP showed that like other global horse and pony breeds the KBP contained mtDNA haplotypes that fell into one of six major haplogroups (A-F, with haplogroup G being mainly confined to a small population of German Senner horses). In the KBP the majority of haplotypes fell into haplogroups C (25%) and E (30%). These two haplogroups appear much less frequently in the global population of horses and ponies (11% and 3% respectively).

Up until our research was conducted, it seemed that the most likely origin of the KBP was the more southerly regions of Europe, namely Spain and the Iberian Peninsula. This theory is most likely to have developed because the closest geographical neighbour to the KBP, the Connemara Pony (CP), has had long standing connections to Spain. It is believed that the CP descended from the Spanish Barb and other Celtic breeds. Like the CP, the majority of the mtDNA sequences from horses throughout the rest of the world are contained in two haplogroups: A (36%) and D (30%). However, the haplogroup frequency variation detected in the KBP makes it more likely that the founding KBP population originated in the more Northern regions

Photo © Pascal Lando

of Europe and Scandinavia, where, like the KBP, many ponies native to these regions share higher proportions of haplogroups C and E than is seen elsewhere in the world.

Combining both nuclear and mitochondrial DNA studies, our findings indicate that genetically, the KBP is closer to the Welsh pony than to its geographically closest neighbour, the CP. The KBP is more closely related to the Northern European breeds such as the Icelandic and Shetland pony breeds, which would suggest that its origins lay in Northern Europe as opposed to Southern Europe. The genetic status of the breed stands in good stead regarding genetic diversity and differentiation and with proper breeding management it can be concluded that the future of this breed can be safely conserved.

HISTORY AND ORIGINS

Mary McGrath & Gay Keogh

The story of the Kerry Bog Pony is nothing short of extraordinary. At several periods in its history it could have become extinct, like the Erris Pony, the Roscommon Pony, the Cushendall Pony and many other local breeds. But against all odds it has survived into the 21st century. It is not often that a "new breed" is discovered in this day and age but that is the case with the Kerry Bog Pony.

EARLY HISTORY

Although Ireland is perceived as a place with a great connection with the horse, the history of the horse in Ireland is actually quite poorly documented.

Iron Age Ireland was dominated by the spread of the Celts from about 750 B.C. to 50 B.C. The culture was one of many individual groups or communities with constant raiding and battles being fought. There are descriptions of warriors driving into battle in chariots pulled by small horses. Harness pieces in the National Museum of Ireland, dated from this period, fit Kerry Bog Ponies perfectly and so we know that these early ponies were

Clockwise from top: The earliest Irish image of a horse and rider is found in the Book of Kells dating from the 7th century Photo © Trinity College Library

Bronze harness pieces make up the bulk of artefacts recovered from this time. They were usually found in pairs. Image © B. Raftery/National Museum of Ireland

Image from the High Cross at Ahenny, Co Tipperary showing a pair of ponies pulling a chariot with spoked wheels accompanied by two ridden ponies.

around 11 – 12 hands high. Archaeological finds are rare from the Iron Age but some horse bones have been documented from sites at Newgrange and Tara. Some of these bones would suggest an animal of up 11–13hh.

The earliest illustration we have of a horse in Ireland is in the 7th century Book of Kells, where a man is depicted riding a very small horse.

Illustrations on High Crosses in Offaly, Meath and Tipperary, carved during the 8th to the 10th century, show small horses being ridden and pulling chariots in pairs.

Horses obviously existed at this time but they would have been a luxury and a prized possession, they were not yet commonplace. Bronze harness

Art MacMurrrough riding bareback and shoeless on his famous small horse to meet the invading Normans who wore armour and rode their larger horses with saddles and stirrups Image © The British Library

pieces found, such as bits and "leading pieces", would have been very expensive – they would have cost many cows to purchase and would have been conspicuous signs of wealth.

The Viking invasions of Ireland, between 795 A.D. and 1000 A.D. could be a significant chapter in the development of the Kerry Bog Pony, given the Northern European origins pointed to in the genetic analysis of Chapter 2.

Viking settlements were established on Beginish, Dingle Bay and Limerick on the Southwest coast of Ireland. It is an accepted fact that Vikings transported ponies throughout their realm. The well documented Icelandic pony is a clear example of this. This period is examined in more detail in Chapter 4.

With the Norman invasion in 1169 there was an influx of horses from Wales and France. Numbers increased but horses were still a prized asset, only for the wealthy.

The 13th century saw the emergence of the Irish Hobby, a fiery warmblood, considered as a gift fit for a king. In 1399, Art MacMurrough rode to meet the Earl of Gloucester:

"He had a horse without housing or saddle which was so fine and good, that it had cost him, they said, 400 cows.... in coming down he galloped so hard that in my opinion I never saw hare, deer, sheep or any other animal, I declare to you

Image of an Irish
Hobby from 1617
Image © The
Bodleian Library
University of Oxford

with certainty, with such speed, as it did" — *Jean Creton.* (J.Webb 'Translation of the
French metrical history of the description of the deposition of King Richard the Second...'
Archaeologia, 10 (1824).

The Irish hobby was a small horse of about 12 hands that was highly
sought after throughout Europe. On several occasions in the 15th, 16th and
17th centuries the export of Hobbies from Ireland was banned. Great
landlords such as the Earl of Cork and the Duke of Ormonde had stud
farms where Hobbies were bred. They were exported for racing and would
have been used to "improve" many local types.

They seem to have become extinct in the late 17th century. The term
'hobby' was in use throughout the country at one time but later came to be
used only in the far west and in Kerry where it endures up to the present day.

SURVIVAL DESPITE THE ODDS

Traditionally, a horse or pony evolves over time, eventually becoming a type,
governed by its suitability for use for a specific task and influenced by its

environs and its geographical limitations. Our knowledge of how the small ponies of Kerry developed is based mostly on conjecture.

Historical accounts of the Kerry Bog Pony are scarce. From the 16th century on, occasional tantalising references occur about the small pony used in Kerry. The pony itself is rarely the subject under discussion; it is usually a presence in the background. That it has survived into the 21st century to become a scientifically recognised breed is remarkable as there were several well-documented occasions, over the last few centuries when such an insignificant pony, which was never present in large numbers, was threatened with extinction.

In the 16th century, it is recorded that invading armies took horses and cattle as spoils of war and drove them away towards Dingle to be exported. In this way Kerry was almost denuded of animals throughout the 16th century.

The Black Earl's Raid on Corkaguiny AD 1580

"The Earl of Ormonde, being Lord Governoure of Munster, never slept his time, but was always in readiness, being the first with the foremost and the last with the hindermost. His lordship minding to follow a piece of service, divideth his compagnie into two parties, the one he took himself and took the ware of the island (Castleisland), and the other he appointed to go directlie to Traleigh (Tralee), and there they met and marched to Dingle-a-Cush, and as they went they drove the whole countrie before them into the Ventrie (Ventry), and by that means they pried and took alle the cattell in the countrie, to the number of eight thousand kine, besides horses, garrons, shepe and goats, and all such people as they met they did without mercie put to the sword. By this means the whole countrie having no cattell nor kine left, they were driven to such extremities that for want of vittels they were either to die and perish for famine, or to die under the sword." (Hooker's Chronicle, AD 1580)

These were unsettled political times. This account of the aftermath of the great Battle of Kinsale indicates the existence and probable use of the Kerry Bog Pony in the 17th century:

After the Battle of Kinsale in 1641 the Irish fled North towards the safety of Ulster pursued by Sir George Wilmot, Queen's Governor of Bere. O'Sullivan Beare, mounted on his favourite horse An Cearc, led the retreat. 'Conceive the difficulty of moving a column of 1000 persons through the wildest country, when snow and ice and flood make all the ways difficult. The soldiers...number something over 400, of whom 13 are mounted,

45

and the rest infantry, musketeers and pikemen. ... There are some women and other non-combatants in the column... there are wagons with the general accoutrements of encampment, besides goods and chattels of men who expect never to see Munster again; and a number of draught horses — probably Kerry ponies of the old native breed, useful in mountain travel. On the first day this column moved not less than 26 miles over the mountaintops northward to Kilgarvan.' (*Beara to Breifne — the Great Retreat.* Donal O Siodhachain ed. Clo Dunaire/Irish and Celtic Publications, Cork 1987)

During the 17th and 18th centuries, ownership of land in Kerry changed hands as the power struggles between English settlers and the Irish fluctuated back and forth. Much of the population became tenants on smallholdings, which ranged in size from 1 acre up to 30 acres. Often the larger holdings were on marginal land. Only the wealthier of these holdings could afford to keep a pony for transport and to work on the land. Under the Penal Laws Catholics were not allowed to keep a horse worth more than £5.00 which further ensured the use of small ponies of lesser value.

PENAL LAWS

Sec. 10. No papist shall be capable of having or keeping for his use, any horse, gelding or mare of five pounds value. Any protestant who shall make discovery under oath of such horse, shall be authorized with the assistance of a constable, to search for and secure such horse and in case of resistance to break down any door. And any protestant making such discovery and offering five pounds five shillings to the owner of such horse, in the presence of a justice of the peace or chief magistrate, shall receive ownership of such horse as though such horse were bought in the market overt.

Will III c.5 (1695): An Act for the better securing the government, by disarming papists

In the 18th century, in accounts from visitors to Kerry we find mention of small ponies being used to carry goods in mountainous areas of the Cork/ Kerry border. Roads were non-existent and the ponies came into their own in navigating the terrain, either ridden or pulling a Slide Car or Sleamhnán. (As the name suggests these travelled on slides instead of wheels, which would have been useless on the mountainy terrain.)

In 1756, Dr Charles Smith, Dublin, wrote of the small local pony in his account of the County of Kerry:

"The little hobbies of the country are the properest horses to travel through it; and a man must abandon himself intirely to their guidance, which will answer much better than if one should strive to manage and direct their footsteps; for these creatures are a sort of automata or machines ... which naturally follow the laws of mechanics, and will conduct themselves much better on those occasions, than the most knowing persons can possibly direct them.

I have already observed, that the horses in these baronies, are naturally very surefooted; they are small, but an excellent breed; they climb over the most rugged rocks, and both ascend and descend the steepest precipices with great facility and safety; are so light, as to skim over waving bogs and morasses without sinking, where heavier horses would certainly perish. They are strong and durable, easily supported and not ill shaped; so hardy as to stand abroad all winter, and will browse on heath, furze and other shrubs; add to this their gait is ambling, which is extremely easy." (pp142/3, *Antient & Present State of co. of Kerry*, Dr. Charles Smith, Dublin 1756).

POPULATION

If we allow four and a half or five persons to each house in this county, which ...seems to be nearest the truth: we shall find that as in this present year 1754 there are by the said returns but 10,228 houses in this county there can be but 51,140 people in it: a number considerably less than the city of Cork contains and very few for an extent of 1,030,193 English acres of land viz upwards of 20 acres for each person.
P.78 The Antient and Present State of the County of Kerry Dr Charles Smith Dublin 1756

In the 18th century the potato had already become a staple of the smallholder diet in Kerry. During the winter of 1741 there was a prolonged period of extreme cold and frost. This was followed by a summer of drought and another freezing winter. Great numbers of livestock froze to death. The potatoes froze and then rotted in the ground. The results of these losses were catastrophic. It is said that one third of all cottiers (the poorest form of tenant farmers), over

19th Century oil painting of a family group and their pony collecting seaweed on the foreshore Image courtesy of James Adams Art Auctions.

300,000 souls, perished in Munster — one fifth of the entire population. In south Kerry this period had a greater effect on the population than the Great Famine. Despite these disasters, some of the hardiest ponies survived and ensured the continued existence of the little pony in Kerry.

By the 19th century, smallholdings kept a pig or a goat and some hens and the potato was the prevalent crop grown. Lime and seaweed had to be carried inland on horseback to fertilise and improve the soil.

In the north of Kerry large herds of black cows, which were known for their milk, were found. The Kerry cow also still survives today.

"The principal products of this county are butter, beef, hides and tallow. The northern parts of the county produce chiefly fat cattle for the markets of Cork; and the southern parts support vast quantities of small cattle and young stock."
(p.75 Charles Smith ibid)

Many families had to carry heavy loads themselves as they couldn't afford to keep a pony. Photo © National Photographic Archive

HIDES AND TALLOW

"The by-products of the cattle trade were many...There were two products which towered above the others: tallow and cattle skins." Cattle skins were exported as "green" or untanned, cured or tanned hides or calfskins which were always shipped out in an untanned state. Tallow was the result of melted down fatty products from the slaughterhouse. It was manufactured into soap or candles.

"An estimate of 1741 as to the relative values of the produce of a bullock suggested 58.6 % for the meat, 23.7% for the hide and 17.8% for the tallow."

Old World Colony – Cork and South Munster 1630-1830 p141

Estate owners ploughed with cattle and used larger horses for riding or pulling a travelling vehicle. Poorer families who could barely afford a cow or a pig were not in a position to keep a horse or even a donkey or small pony; the very poor used manual labour to till the land.

Map of Kerry
showing some of the
main routes of the
Butter Road to Cork

Opposite: During
the 19th Century
new roads were
built which rendered
many of the twisting
mountain trackways
obsolete. Photo ©
Michael Diggin

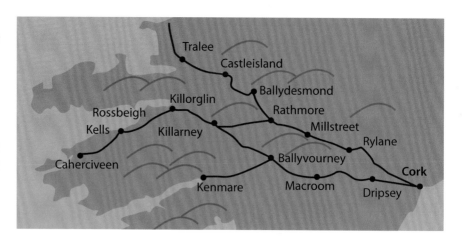

So it would seem that a limited number of small farmers, with perhaps 15 to 30 acres, could afford the upkeep of a small pony. They were used to carry loads in creels or pull slide cars where there were no roads. They carried fish from Dingle to the market in Tralee and butter from all over Kerry to the butter market in Cork. The sale of butter in Cork was the major source of earnings for those smallholders who were able to keep milking cows on their restricted acres. Butter was packed into Firkins and transported to Cork via Millstreet or Macroom. From Castleisland this journey took four days each way. This vital role for the Kerry Bog Pony lasted until the establishment of a road network at which time the butter was transported by cart using a larger draught horse.

BUTTER MARKET & FIRKINS

The Cork Butter Market opened in 1770 and continued trading for 150 years. It was so important at one time that the world price of butter was determined by the price of butter in Cork. The salted butter was brought to the market in caskets called "firkins" made of good hardwood. Butter and soap used to be sold by the firkin. In these cases it was a measure of weight, instead of volume: e.g., 56 lb (25.4 kg) and 64 lb (29.0 kg) respectively. Butter was brought by pack horses and later by horse drawn cart from West Cork and Kerry along routes known as butter-roads. The journey to Cork took up to 4 days each way.

Photo © Pascal Lando

Butter was carried
to the Butter Market
in hardwood barrels
called firkins

TRAVELLERS' TALES

During the 18th and 19th centuries we have accounts from a number of
sources of visits, tours and studies of Co. Kerry. During this period of
history it was very fashionable to do walking tours of such scenic areas. These
early tourists provide the best descriptions of the Kerry Bog Pony and are
really the only types of records available that actually confirm the existence
of this little local pony.

A French gentleman named Coquebert described the Kerry he found
during his visit in 1790:

> " *For transport these people still use the carr sleamhnain or sliding car, almost to
> the exclusion of the trockle, or cart on wheels, the former vehicle being better suited
> to a roadless terrain of perilous heights, soft sands and turf-bogs. ...The typical
> Kerry horse at £5.00 is a small black animal called a hobby. Bay or brown horses
> are very scarce in the county. Saddles, called straddles, are made of straw, as also
> are harnesses, though some of these are of horse-hair.*" (New View of Eighteenth Century
> Kerry, Sile Ni Chinneide p 85)

Opposite:
A traveller's view of
the Gap of Dunloe
in 1859, showing
tourists riding small
Kerry Bog Ponies.
Note the ladies riding
sidesaddle and the
man carrying
a bugle

Almost a century later an English visitor wrote:

"I spent 2 days in and about Kenmare — one of them a long summer's day, mounted on a Kerry Pony riding down the opposite side of the Kenmare River — riding and walking in and out among the mountain glens and traversing the greater part of the Barony of Glanrought. I had a double enjoyment in the ramble: arising both from the charming weather and fine mountain views, and from the spectacle of a rapidly improving country and a comparatively comfortable population." (Ireland in 1834 , Henry D. Inglis: London, Whittaker and Co., Ave Maria Lane 1835)

"BLOW BUGLE BLOW"

Certain areas of Kerry provide world renowned echo conditions. In the nineteenth century the bugle was part of the Tourist experience and was blown in the Gap of Dunloe and on the Lakes of Killarney.

"When visitors ascend the pass to the Gap of Dunloe from Kate Kearney's Cottage the guide walks beside the ponies reciting verses about Killarney, and when the gloomy Pass is reached he makes the walls of MacGillicuddy's Reeks echo with Irish Airs played on his bugle. He explains that he does this as his father did before him."

Near the boathouse is a spot from whence the effect of a bugle with the mouth directed to Ross Castle, infinitely exceeds any other echo to be met with about the lakes; the first echo is returned from the Castle, the second from the ruined church of Aghadoe, the third from Mangerton, afterwards innumerable reverberations are distinguished, which appear like the faded brilliancy of an extremely multiplied refelexion lost by distance and repetition.

Guide to the Lakes of Killarney Rev.GN Wright AM London 1822

The intrepid Mr and Mrs S. C. Hall undertook an extensive tour around Ireland and of Kerry they wrote:

"The journey to the summit of Mangerton is not to be thought of lightly ... we commenced our excursion on a morning that gave promise of a fine day;

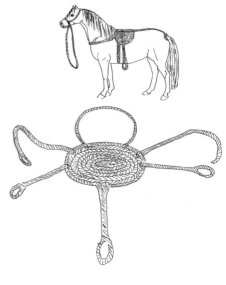

Left: Mrs Hall's
"Kerry Dragoon"

Right: Drawing of
straw harness in the
National Museum
of Country Life,
Castlebar

mounted on the sure-footed ponies whom "practice hath made perfect" and who are never known to stumble .. The sure feet of our horses were soon tried; the little roughcoated animals had to make their way over rocks, bogs and huge stones, through rushing and brawling streams and along the brinks of precipices — places where it would be very difficult for persons unaccustomed to mountain travelling to move along on foot. At length we reached the Devil's Punch Bowl.

...we observed a singular character watching our movements; it was one of the Kerry peasants mounted on a small active pony, sitting in front of a pair of hampers, in which he had conveyed his tubs of butter to the market in Cork, from which he was now returning. The hampers were fastened to the horse by a rope of hay; and his bridle, which was merely twisted round the nose of the animal, was made of the same material. In this primitive style he galloped up and down hills as fearlessly and far more safely than a steed fully caparisoned for the chase. We learned that he was one of a class known in cities and towns by the cognomen of "Kerry Dragoons". We made a sketch of him and introduce him to our readers."(Ireland — *its Scenery, Character etc,* by Mr & Mrs S.C.Hall 1841 Vol. I London — How and Parson)

A German visitor to Kerry observed:

"The Gap of Dunloe. This the traveller reaches by going round the end of the lower lake and a few miles further to the gap. Then he mounts his pony and rides across the mountain on the other side of which he arrives at the extreme end of the upper lake.

The Kerry horses, like all horses of a mountainous country, are small but sagacious, cautious and hardy. Their harness for want of leather, flax or any better material is composed of straw and is the poorest I ever met with.

Straw ropes are used everywhere throughout Ireland, and it is very usual to see one tied round the leg of a pig as it is driven to market. (Describes goats, pigs and even hens spancelled to keep them on the family's small holding and to prevent them from trespassing on the neighbouring land) ...I never saw before an entire harness of plaited straw; and what is more remarkable is, that it was not a mere makeshift or the whim of an individual, but the general custom throughout the whole west of Ireland. (P131 Travels in Ireland , J.G.Kohl London 1844 Translated from the German)

The road which afterwards runs in many winding ways over Turk mountain, has been only recently found, and passes through one of the most desolate and wildest regions in the west of Ireland, which for thousands of years before our time had only been traversed by those little mountain horses with straw bridles." (P 143 Travels in Ireland , J.G.Kohl London 1844 Translated from the German)

Then came The Great Famine of 1845–1852. Localised failures of the potato crop occurred in Kerry up to the mid 1850s. This extended period of deprivation caused extreme poverty among those smallholders who survived. Evictions were widespread. Census figures show that the population of Kerry declined by 19% between 1841 and 1851 with a further drop in population figures of 22.87% between 1851 and 1861 due to death and emigration.

In the aftermath of the famine, farm holdings altered in size, the 15 to 30 acre holding largely disappeared, resulting in the consolidation of the large estates and proliferation of small holdings too poor to sustain any grazing animals.

19th Century
Eviction Scenes
from Glenbeigh, Co
Kerry. The thatch
was set on fire.
Note the battering
ram to break
down the walls.
Photo © National
Photographic Archive

Figures extracted
from Census results
highlight the
dramatic change in
farm stock numbers
as a result of the
Great Famine

CHANGE IN ANIMAL HOLDINGS BETWEEN 1841 AND 1847

Size of Farm	Horses and Mules		Asses		Cattle	
	increase	Decrease	Increase	Decrease	Increase	Decrease
Under 1 acre		28219		17405		67168
From 1-5 acres		63678		12593		200280
From 5-15 acres		74225	25234			164555
From 15-30 acres	22186		16858		89638	
Over 30 acres	130222		22033		541622	
	152408	166122	64125	29998	631260	432003
	Decrease 13,714		Increase 34,127		Increase 199,257	

Size of Farm	Sheep		Pigs		Poultry	
	Increase	Decrease	Increase	Decrease	Increase	Decrease
Under 1 acre		100678		323337		1850632
From 1-5 acres		203109		228882		1383946
From 5-15 acres		213243		260881		982921
From 15-30 acres		2918		82026	207276	
Over 30 acres	600306		107687		1253575	
	600306	519948	107687	895126	1460851	4217499
	Increase 80,358		Decrease 787,439		Decrease 2,756,648	

Those tenants or smallholders who remained on the land could barely afford a pig or a cow. During the famine years horses and ponies disappeared from most small farms in Ireland. In Kerry their numbers declined drastically. One can only speculate how the Kerry Bog Pony survived these times. Never widespread, perhaps its presence in scattered pockets around the county ensured the survival of some ponies in less badly affected areas.

This image of Sir Peter George FitzGerald, 19th Knight of Kerry, 1st Baronet of Valentia (1808–1880) riding a Kerry Bog Pony, shows that the ponies were still being used in the 19th century even by the wealthy and this may have resulted in the survival of some breeding stock.

The Knight of Kerry riding a Kerry Bog Pony

TRANSATLANTIC CABLE

In 1866 the first transatlantic cable was successfully laid. It was 2.5" in diameter and stretched from Newfoundland to Valentia Island a distance of over 2300 miles. At 20 tons per mile laying this cable was obviously a huge undertaking. It linked up with the telegraph to Dublin which in turn was connected to England and the continent. It was now possible to get a reply from North America the same day. Until the first transatlantic cable was laid the communications between Europe and the United States took about a week.

By 1886 conditions may have improved as an account of land holding in Munster stated:

"Butter and young stock and the smaller class of horses are produced plentifully on the poorer mountain lands".(Morgan John O'Connell, 1886, *Munster Land-Owning*, W. Ridgeway, London. p 15)

These small horses were also known as Gearons (from Gearr which means short in Irish). They were small compared to the usual type of packhorses that were found in and around the local towns. Their strength lay in their hardiness and sure-footedness, which enabled them to work in the hills and mountains and survive on the grasses, herbs and bushes that grew there.

The area of south Kerry around the Gap of Dunloe, Kenmare, Valentia, Killorglin and the hills around Dingle was the main stronghold of the Kerry Bog Pony. However, they do not seem to have been widespread or to have existed in large numbers at any stage.

> *"Kerry: The occupations are dairy-farming, tillage, and fishing. The dairy stock generally is of a good description, and the sheep of the mountain kind. The small native Kerry cattle are much esteemed as milchers. Numerous herds of goats are fed on the mountains; ponies of a superior description are occasionally offered for sale. Some of the wilder mountains are still haunted by the red deer."* (Guy's Postal Directory of Munster 1886)

Ironically, in the mid to late 19th century, the new road network that was built in order to provide employment and income during the famine years, was the next threat to the survival of the pony. The improved surfaces allowed the use of larger, faster horses, capable of carrying heavier loads. The role of the small sure-footed ponies as pack animals was no longer an economic necessity.

Smuggled goods were carried over mountain pathways to avoid the Excise men

Perhaps what saved it on this occasion was the introduction of new Excise Duties on alcohol and other goods! A small but significant role for the ponies evolved as transport for the smuggling trade, evading inspection by travelling secret and little-known mountain trails, carrying their precious cargoes.

PUCK FAIR

Puck Fair is held in Killorglin, Co. Kerry , every year from the 10th to the 12th of August. It has been held annually for over 400 years.

"Its speciality is horseflesh, of which there is generally a good supply of varying degrees of excellence or otherwise. The fair, is held annually on the 11th of August, but the day previous and the day following are quite as important and the fair day; the three days being known as the "Gathering day", the "Fair day" and the "Scattering day", respectively."

The Irish Times, *letter dated 21st June 1917, from Mr Edward Twiss, of Kilmacow, Co. Kilkenny.*

The existence of the pony in Kerry in the early 20th century is shown in the following extract from a letter to *The Irish Times* where it is mentioned and given equal importance alongside the Kerry Cow and the Mountain Sheep.

"....on Gathering day flocks and herds are driven in from all sides of Kerry. The sturdy, shaggy, sure- footed Kerry Pony, full of life (and a long life at that), the diminutive black cattle.....; handsome little fellows those Kerry cattle are full of 'spirit and divilment' as the man said when one of them drove his horns trough a barrel of porter that he was tethered near. Next comes a herd of mountain sheep...sheep no bigger than a terrier...; able to leap and run like a greyhound, they bound and skelter in all directions, under carts, through horses legs', jumping obstacles several times their own height, through the drovers shouting, whistling and execrating." (Irish Times letter, 21st June 1917 from Mr Edward Twiss, of Kilmacow, Co. Kilkenny)

More recently, in the 1930s, farming came under great pressure. Families struggled for survival during the Economic War when the export of cattle and goods to England collapsed. The price of cattle fell and subsistence farming became the order of the day. Poor cottiers returned to the use of the spade to cultivate their small plots of land. Emigration increased. A pony

Carts carrying milk churns were once a common sight snaking along the roads to the creamery. Photo © Bord Fáilte

became an unaffordable luxury for many. The advance of mechanisation and the introduction of the tractor in the 1950s and 60s brought yet another threat to the survival of the humble Kerry Bog Pony. No longer would lines of ponies and carts be seen queuing outside the creamery each morning.

Despite the many factors mitigating against the survival of this small insignificant pony some Kerry Bog Ponies did indeed survive. One of these was "The Bogman", one of the "old type of pony", which was discovered by John Mulvihill in the 1980s on Jim Doyle's farm in Glencar. This was the beginning of the amazing story that has captured worldwide attention – Ireland's third native equine breed, saved from the brink of extinction.

THE VIKING CONNECTION

Mary McGrath & Gay Keogh

Viking longship, the *Sea Stallion,* in full sail Photo: Werner Karrasch ©: The Viking Ship Museum, Denmark

The Kerry Bog Pony has been officially recognised, nationally and internationally, as Ireland's third native equine breed, alongside the Irish Draught Horse and the Connemara Pony. A series of discoveries, one more exciting than the next, have brought us to this point.

All around Ireland there are places where the "old type of pony" mentioned in local stories is no longer to be found. When looked for in south Kerry, they were found to still exist, albeit in dangerously low numbers. When blood typed and genetically tested, it was confirmed that they fulfilled the scientific criteria to be identified as a distinct breed. Then, to further confound us, they were also identified as being more closely related to pony breeds from North Western Europe, Scandinavia and Iceland than to established breeds in Ireland and the UK. The DNA analysis carried out by Weatherbys Laboratory at the Irish Equine Centre proves this. This is not conjecture or theory – it is indisputable, scientific fact.

Unfortunately that is the only fact we can confirm! There are so many unanswered questions. Where did they come from? How did they get to Kerry? Why aren't they found anywhere else in Ireland? How did they survive so long? Where do we start to find the answers?

Looking back through early history, any stories that were written down tended to be records of momentous events such as wars and battles. References to ponies are scarce and give very little detail. Archaeological finds often pose more questions than they answer. We have searched for any historical mentions of ponies in Ireland and given a general account in Chapter 3 – History and Origins.

STARTING POINT

Perhaps a better starting point is the single fact that we do know – the Kerry Bog Pony originated from Northwest Europe and has common ancestry with Scandinavian and Icelandic pony populations. Is it too simplistic to suggest that the Vikings are the common denominator? The facts support this possibility.

While most people's perception of the Vikings is of a bloodthirsty warrior race that invaded Ireland, in fact they were also renowned as seafaring merchants. Their superior boat-building skills and their advanced navigational skills allowed them to travel extensively.

Vikings were wide-ranging explorers and traders

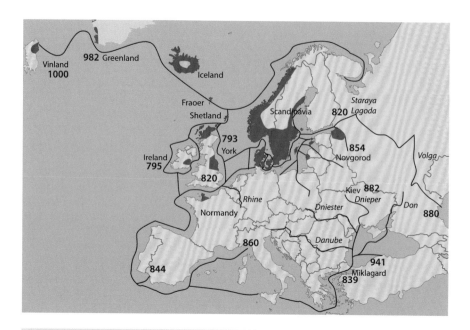

VIKING TRADE ROUTES

Viking trade routes from Scandinavia are known to have stretched down the Danube and Dnieper rivers to the Black Sea and the Caspian Sea, onwards towards Constantinople, through the Straits of Gibraltar, around the Iberian Peninsula into the Mediterranean Sea to Spain, North Africa, Italy, Sicily and across the Atlantic Ocean as far as Greenland and Newfoundland. Trade goods included walrus ivory, glass beads, honey, wool, timber, wheat, furs and pelts, armor, slaves and weapons.

The Vikings were familiar with the west coast of Ireland from the earliest times – in 795 A.D. raids are recorded on Inishmurray and Inishbofin on the north-west coast and Skellig Michael off Kerry.

Settlements are known of on Beginish and Valentia Islands off Kerry. Beginish, with its beautiful sandy beaches, sheltered from the Atlantic by the bulk of Valentia Island, was occupied from the 10th to the 12th century and was believed to be a "longphort" or maritime stopover location. (Sheehan, John, Steffen Stummann Hansen, and Donnchadh Ó Corráin 2001 A Viking Age Maritime Haven: A Reassessment of the Island Settlement at Beginish, Co. Kerry. *The Journal of Irish Archaeology* 10:93-119).

TRADERS OR RAIDERS?

The Viking Age in Ireland started with coastal raids in 795 A.D. and ended early in the 11th century. So for a period of over 200 years the Vikings interacted with the Irish in one form or another. They made Ireland a centre of European trade, introduced the use of money and had a great influence on art, language, folklore and place names.

Left: Viking longship, the *Sea Stallion*, in full sail. Photo Werner Karrasch © The Viking Ship Museum, Denmark.

THE *SEA STALLION*

The *Sea Stallion* is a reconstruction of one of the longest Viking Longships ever found. The original was among five boats, known as the Skuldelev Ships, discovered in 1962 in the Roskilde fjord in Denmark, where they had been buried in the seabed for nearly 950 years. These boats were sunk around 1060, probably to block access to the port.

The longship on which the *Sea Stallion* is modelled is believed to have been built in 1042. Analysis of the timber used in the construction of the boat indicated that it came from Glendalough, Co Wicklow, south of Dublin.

The *Sea Stallion* sailed 1,200 miles from Roskilde, Denmark to Dublin in August 2007. It remained on display in Dublin over the winter before sailing back to Denmark in June, 2008. It is now located in the Viking Ship Museum Harbour in Roskilde, Denmark.

Right: Lying between the Viking settlements of Cork and Limerick, Beginish with its wide sandy beaches was ideally suited as a site for a longphort or stop over station. Photo © Michael Diggin

In the early part of the 9th century, Vikings from Norway began to move west perhaps due to overcrowding in the farming regions, or to strife caused by the impositions of a new king. Not all of these Vikings were raiders, some were farmers and some were merchants. These people brought everything they needed with them, including livestock and ponies. Scattered Viking settlements are found throughout the islands north and west of Scotland, with well-known sites on the Orkneys, the Shetlands, the Hebrides and the Faroes.

Left: Chess Pieces made from walrus ivory found on the Isle of Lewis. Photo © The British Museum

Right: Illustration of Viking Knarr cargo ship showing how animals and goods were transported by sea © National Maritime Museum, Greenwich, London

LEWIS AND ISLAND SETTLEMENTS

The Lewis chessmen were found in the vicinity of Uig on the Isle of Lewis around the 1830s. They were probably made in Norway, about 1150-1200 A.D. At this period, the Western Isles, where the chessmen were buried, were part of the Kingdom of Norway, not Scotland. It seems likely they were buried for safe keeping en route to be traded in Ireland.

The Isle of Lewis in the Outer Hebrides was an important Viking station, from where many of the early raids against Ireland were launched.

The Uists, Barra, Benbecula, Skye, Islay, Colonsay, Oronsay, Arran and Gigha all had Viking stations. To date there is evidence of Viking settlements in Mull, Knapdale and along the shores of Loch Fyne as well. Many of today's village names in Lewis and Skye are of Norse origin.

Merchants would have known all of these settlements and visited regularly to trade. These journeys were only a few days sailing from the west coast of Norway and the islands would also have been used as stop-off points for longer journeys. For the people of Scandinavia, sea journeys were the normal mode of transport, certainly more efficient than overland travel in their coastal regions. While to us the dangers and hardships of such a method of travel appear to be extreme, this was normal life for the time. The Vikings had many classes of boats for different purposes, from the well-known Longships built for speed and war, to the sturdier Knarr or cargo vessels, to the smaller Faering used for short coastal journeys. The boats they used all had shallow keels allowing them to beach easily.

After 840 A.D. they began to settle in Ireland, first in winter bases and later permanently, establishing towns in Dublin, Wexford, Waterford, Cork and Limerick. These were major trade centres and Viking kingdoms. The ruling clans changed often with Norse Vikings, Danish Vikings and Irish clans ruling at different times, especially in Dublin. But elsewhere in many isolated settlements the business of life continued without disruption. The Norse were gradually integrated into the life of the country though they retained close contact with Viking settlements elsewhere. Viking traders continued to travel the coasts of Ireland and beyond.

For their trading missions or settlement journeys the Vikings would have made use of the Knarr which was broader and shorter than the Longship; some were capable of carrying up to 24 tons. This type of boat would have been used in 874 A.D. when a number of Norse Viking clans chose to leave Norway and settle in Iceland.

SETTLEMENT OF ICELAND

Refusing to live under the King of Norway, two "jarls" or clans from Norway emigrated to Iceland at the end of the 9th century. Vikings from Norse settlements in northern Britain and Ireland subsequently joined this Icelandic colonisation and it is known that they brought ponies to Iceland with them from Scotland and Ireland. It could have taken up to two weeks to travel from Norway to Iceland, by the Faroe Islands, depending on the wind and weather conditions.

The stories or sagas of these 9th century settlers are told in records such as the *Íslendingbók* and the *Landnámabók* (meaning "The Book of Settlement") written in the 12th century.

Left: Shetland ponies being transported in small open rowing boat. Photo © Shetland Museum

Right: Cattle at Valentia Island being transported in a similar small open boat. Photo © The Kennelly Archive

This journey across the open Atlantic cannot have been easy. But they were experienced at sea travel, carrying with them all they needed for a new life, including their livestock and ponies. In time, travel between Ireland and Iceland became common. Knarr routinely crossed the North Atlantic carrying livestock and stores to Norse settlements in Iceland and Greenland. We know that sufficient numbers of ponies were brought to Iceland to provide the foundation for today's Icelandic pony. Therefore, we can assume that it would have been possible to transport sufficient numbers of ponies from Scandinavia by boat to establish a presence in Kerry. Even up to the middle of the 20th century cattle and ponies were carried by boat from one land mass to the next. Similar boats and methods were used in Shetland and Ireland.

COINCIDENCE OR EXPLANATION?

When looking for explanations of historic occurrences, it is often found that there is no "great plan" but that things happen for the most mundane of reasons. We know the Vikings travelled from Scandinavia, using islands such as the Scottish isles, the Shetlands, the Hebrides, the Faroes, the Isle of Man and Beginish Island off the Iveragh Peninsula as stopovers and trading posts. What is interesting in the context of the Kerry Bog Pony is that in recent history, many of these isolated locations are known to have had an indigenous type of sturdy pony, adapted to the local conditions. A lot of these, while documented, have now become extinct.

"HIGHLAND PONIES AND SOME REMINISCENCES OF HIGHLAND MEN"

John M.MacDonald, Google Books

Island Ponies

I	The Ponies of Skye	V	The Ponies of Mull
II	The Ponies of Uist	VI	The Ponies of Arran
III	The Ponies of Barra	VII	The Ponies of Lewis and Harris
IV	The Ponies of Rhum	VIII	The Ponies of Tiree
IX	The Ponies of Islay	X	Shetland Ponies

This is the contents page of a late 19th century publication. It shows that, at that time, at least ten different breeds of ponies still survived in the Scottish islands.

SURVIVING PONY BREEDS OF NORTHERN EUROPE

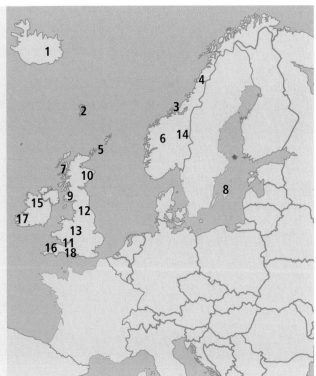

1. Icelandic	10. Highland
2. Faroese	11. Exmoor
3. Fjord	12. Dales
4. NordlandShest	13. Welsh
5. Shetland	14. Dolehest
6. Haflinger	15. Connemara
7. Eriskay	16. Dartmoor
8. Gottland	17. Kerry Bog
9. Fell	18. New Forest

By virtue of its natural geography, areas of south Kerry were to all intents and purposes another "island" completely isolated by the natural boundaries of the sea and mountains. Until 1822, when Richard Griffith began a major road building plan in Kerry, the only access was over isolated mountain trails, either on foot or on horseback.

Why are the ponies to be found in Kerry and not elsewhere along the Irish coast? Perhaps they were in other locations but did not survive in sufficient numbers to remain a distinct type. We just don't know.

MANX PONIES

Manx ponies also became extinct c. 1820-1830. Of them Thomas Quayle said:

"The island had formerly its peculiar breed also of ponies, fine boned, sure footed; blacks, greys, and bays: from neglect this breed also has become nearly extinct. Still less care than with regard to horned cattle and sheep, has been taken to replace the indigenous breed by the introduction of good draft-horses. In the uplands a small breed is yet to be found, kept at slender expense, rarely housed in winter. When wanted, they are fetched home in the morning, and after a feed of sheaf-oats or hay, worked all day, and in the evening, after another feed, dismissed again to the pasture. The animal thus treated must be unequal to the spring-ploughing; but from the cessation of work in summer, gradually recovers."

General View Of The Agriculture of The Isle of Man. London 1812

If ponies were brought to Beginish by Viking traders, it would have been because there was a demand for them. They must have fulfilled a purpose or very quickly evolved and adapted to meet the requirements of the people living in South-west Kerry. The Kerry Bog pony, small in number as well as stature, was certainly shaped by its purpose, its location and its isolation.

Photo © Fáilte Ireland

HISTORY OF THE KERRY BOG PONY CO-OPERATIVE SOCIETY

Mary McGrath & Gay Keogh

Top: John Mulvihill
Bottom: Robert
Donaldson

The extraordinary story of the rediscovery of the Kerry Bog Pony was the result of a number of coincidences and the single vision of one man.

John Mulvihill, whose family came from Listowel, Co. Kerry, was the first person to identify the possibility that an old breed of ponies might exist. Sometime in the 1980s John's sister, historian, Joan Stack, had introduced him to the works of Charles Smith and Isaac Ware where, in the 18th century, mention was made of native Kerry ponies. They idly wondered at the time if any had any survived into the 20th century?

Then in the mid-1980s John Mulvihill met Robert and Esther Donaldson from Enniskillen, Co. Fermanagh, and they spoke about the Cushendall Pony, a type of cob, which by that time was thought to be extinct. Robert had been searching the North of Ireland in an attempt to discover if any survived on the land. This prompted John to wonder whether he might find any survivors of the "lost" breed of Kerry Ponies. He began to ask around to see if anyone remembered them. John's own father, Jer Mulvihill, who owned a turf yard in Listowel, had remembered small ponies which were referred to as hobbies. Dr Brian McMahon, An Máistir, told how his father had used a pony to draw in turf from the bog. John B. Keane, the renowned playwright and publican, recalled such ponies taking milk to the creamery and being driven into town for shopping. There was much anecdotal evidence from older farmers about the existence of a small native working breed of pony. They had no great value and were used to perform the same work as donkeys.

Around the same time John heard about a stallion owned by Jim Doyle from Glencar, who refered to it as "one of the old ponies". When he went to see the pony he was struck by what he saw. This little stallion did not look like a Shetland pony, nor a Welsh pony. It was a strong powerful compact working pony, already quite old and not in the best condition. The work was hard as the farm was on a hillside but the pony pulled "a horse's load". John bought the stallion for £300 with half a crown back for luck.

LUCK MONEY

This is an amount given back to the buyer by the seller on the completion of a deal, for luck. It is a tradition at Irish fairs and sales where it is intended to bring the buyer luck with his purchase.

This pony became the first 'Bogman'. Once he arrived at the Red Fox Inn he was wormed and fed on a diet of mashes with Guinness and three eggs and their crushed shells every day. The great racehorse Arkle was known to eat the same food and if it was good enough for Arkle it was good enough for the Bogman.

To begin with the Bogman had no interest in mares and there were worries that he might be too old to begin a stud career. Then Mick Teahan, from Dooks, brought a little chestnut mare called Josie to the Bogman and after some time she went in foal. This foal was Dempsey Bog which has since been exported to the United States. The Bogman also bred a number of other foals. At that time bloodtyping was not carried out and so these foals were not clearly identified. Dempsey Bog was mated to Purple Heather and Flashy Fox, foaled in 1992, was their offspring.

John bought the stallion, Dempsey Bog, from Johnny Courtney in Faha and sought out some mares from farmers and fairs throughout south-west Kerry. In 1993 one of the ponies injured its leg and was brought to the vet –

Daniel Hutch MRCVS, from Kanturk, who immediately recognised the quality of the pony. Sometime later John brought another pony to the vet who once again was struck by its temperament and conformation. He wondered what breed they were and John told him of his search for the "old breed". Daniel Hutch suggested that bloodtyping would provide more information and advised him to contact Dr John Flynn in Weatherbys at the Irish Equine Centre.

By the early 1990s John had recruited vet Teddy Clifford MRCVS to look at the ponies and identify their unique traits. The search for ponies was publicised by *The Kerryman, Kerry's Eye* and by Radio Kerry. John enlisted the help of friends Tim Cooper and the Teahans to attend many horse fairs around Kerry and the neighbouring counties to find suitable ponies which were selected on the basis of type and size. John bought a number of these in order to create a herd of 10 – 12 ponies. Old Peat for example was bought at Puck Fair but he had previously come from Cape Clear Island. Teddy and John drew up a Breed Standard for the first intake of ponies in 1992. They were weighed and measured. Type, that intangible quality, was most important. Shetland and Welsh qualities were excluded; the ponies taken in were small, working ponies.

Teddy Clifford looked at all the early intake of ponies and was impressed with their great constitutions. They were extremely sound with no evidence of laminitis, respiratory diseases or sweet itch. They had rarely been wormed but their grazing was very varied and wide ranging. They browsed over rough terrain eating a diet of grasses, rushes, herbs, furze, etc. As they grazed alongside

Left: Teddy Clifford MRCVS
Right: Tim Cooper

EARLY MEMBERS LIST

Breen, Jim. Glowncapee, Kilgobnet, Beaufort, Co. Kerry

Calder Potts, Hylton. Highbank Farm, Cuffesgrange, Co. Kilkenny

Cooper, Tim. Droum Headford, Killarney, Co. Kerry

Courtney, John. Doonkinane, Faha, Killarney, Co. Kerry

De Las Casas, Michael. Larch Hill, Kilcock, Co. Kildare

Davis, Michael. Kilmihill, Ballingary, Co. Limerick

Desmond, Michelle. Lower Behaghane, Castlecove, Killarney, Co. Kerry

Donaldson, Robert. Raceview House, Factory Road, Enniskillen, Co. Fermanagh

Fogarty, Seamus. Rockfield, Tralee Road, Killarney, Co. Kerry

Gerathy, Tom. Red Hill, Ballyvary, Castlebar, Co. Mayo

Gschwendtner, Mr & Mrs. Ballymurphy, Kilfenora, Co. Clare

Hayes, Paul & Anne. River View, Bray Road, Enniskerry, Co. Wicklow

Hoare, Claire. Tullymore, Killorglin, Co. Kerry

Lowe, Michael. Rathmore, Co. Kerry

Lynch, Batt & Mary. Urlee, Lisselton, Listowel, Co. Kerry

McGovern, Eugene & Anne. 86 Tamlacht Road, Omagh, Co. Tyrone

Maher, Denis. Mount Pleasant Farm, Rathoath, Co. Meath

Maher, Jane. Caherdaniel, Co. Kerry

Morris, John. Droumbrain, Glencar, Co. Kerry

Murray, Paul. Glencuttane, Glencar, Co. Kerry

Mulvihill, John. Kerry Bog Village, Glenbeigh, Co. Kerry

Nagle, Daniel. Rathbeg, Rathmore, Co. Kerry

Noonan, Martin. Bog View Stud, Barra Diuma, Castlebar, Co. Mayo

O'Connell, William. Ballyfineen, Grenagh, Co. Cork

O'Connell, Diarmuid. Ballyfineen, Grenagh, Co. Cork

O'Donovan, Bartlemy. Fermoy, Co. Cork

Stack, Joan. Old Forge Cottage, Greenville, Listowel, Co. Kerry

Teahan, Michael. Dooks, Glenbeigh, Co. Kerry

Wall, David. (formerly of) 14 Ashton Lawn, Knocklyon Road, Templeogue, Dublin 16

Whitten, Willian & Thelma. Birr, Co. Offaly

Left:L Michael
Teahan Snr
Right: Michael
Teahan Jnr

cattle and were not overstocked they did not suffer from bad worm infestations. They were free moving, very correct, compact and powerful for their size. Their temperament was outstanding with no obvious vices – the result of many generations of working closely with farmers on the land and the bogs.

Tim Cooper recalled the ponies that he had used to bring milk to the creamery and had often paired with a horse when mowing hay many years ago. One day at a fair at Newmarket, Co. Cork Tim saw this "small handy pony" tied to a gate whereupon he made the deal and brought home 'Quagmire Prince'. He admits that he did not know much about this "old breed" but he recognised that this pony was different and something special. In promoting the Kerry Bog Pony Tim brought Quagmire Prince to the Kildare County Show in Athy in 1995 and also to Tinehely, Co. Wicklow. In this way many people got their first glimpse of a Kerry Bog Pony and the existence of the breed was widely publicised.

The Teahan family has always kept ponies. Michael Teahan Snr remembers working with ponies on the bog and bringing milk to the creamery from the seven or eight cows they kept on the farm. They always had a small pony and sometimes a larger pony as well.

KERRY PONY SOCIETY

The Kerry Pony Society drew up a Register of Mares and Stallions In 1971. The ponies listed ranged in height from 11hh to 14.2hh. and were of whole colours only. Nowadays the Kerry Pony Society holds a successful annual show at Blenerville, Co. Kerry with an extensive range of showing and showjumping classes for ponies of all types.

He remembers how they used to have races for ponies and carts in Killorglin. They had heats of three ponies at a time with a final run off. These races took place on a level road outside the town. Mick still drives a pony, the little mare November whose mother was out of Josie, the original mare mated to the Bogman. Michael Teahan Jnr continues the family tradition and has a Kerry Bog Pony Stud in Dooks, Co. Kerry.

Ponies continued to be brought to the Red Fox Inn and John selected suitable animals by type, size, colour, temperament and movement. John, acting on vet Dan Hutch's suggestion, spoke to Dr John Flynn from Weatherbys DNA Laboratory. Dr Flynn had heard John on the Pat Kenny Show on the radio and he was very enthusiastic about the project. He offered to bloodtype the ponies free of charge and build up a database of information. Starting in 1994 all ponies were bloodtyped and later DNA typed. Gene frequency calculations were carried out on the identified genetic markers in the population. These calculations provide a powerful means of segregating and establishing equine breeds.

"BLACK PASSPORTS"

Dr Leo Curran advised John to keep records of pedigrees with a view to having the breed recognised in the long term. By this time John had ordered Passport type documents from Killarney Printing. Approved ponies had their markings taken and were bloodtyped by Weatherbys. "Black Passports" or

Left: Dr John Flynn
Right: Dr Leo Curran

82

pedigree information documents were issued to each pony that had been marked and bloodtyped.

The first Kerry Bog Pony Society was founded in 1992 at which time there were 20 known mares and 6 stallions. Meetings were held by an enthusiastic group of pony owners who shared John Mulvihill's vision of a potentially old breed rediscovered. Michele Desmond, Society secretary at that time, provided much information about the early days of the conservation effort.

KERRY BOG PONY SOCIETY OF IRELAND
Officers of First Committee 1994
Chairperson: John Mulvihill
Vice chairperson: Seamus Fogarty
Secretary: Michelle Desmond
Assistant Secretary: Claire Hoare
Treasurer: Joan Mulvihill Stack
Joint Treasurer: John Courtney
Public Relations Officer: Anne Hayes
Joint Public Relations Officer: Robert Donaldson

Michelle Desmond

For over 10 years John Mulvihill issued "Black Passports" or information documents for each pony approved by him. These included many with no known breeding and all these ponies became known as Foundation Stock. These "Black Passports" were issued from 1992 to 2002.

Simultaneously, efforts were being made to have the breed formally recognised. In the early days, despite determined efforts, little progress was made.

People outside of Kerry began to take an interest in these native ponies. Robert Donaldson of Co. Fermanagh, Arlene Aston of Co. Down, and Eugene McGovern of Co. Tyrone, introduced the breed into Northern Ireland. Rachel Sterling and Norma Cook, both past secretaries of the Society, bred ponies in Tipperary and Wicklow and the Calder-Potts family in Co. Kilkenny also had a number of ponies. Peter Keyes of Blue Ball, Co. Offaly effectively promoted The Kerry Bog Pony especially through his association with the Tullamore Show.

Left: Eugene
McGovern
Right: Pat Byrne

Having read an article in the *Irish Farmers Journal* in 2002, Pat Byrne became interested in the Kerry Bog Pony and bought his first animal that same year. He had a deep interest in pedigrees and breeding and was appointed Keeper of the Studbook in the Kerry Bog Pony Society. He was later elected to the same position in the newly formed Co-operative Society, a position he held until 2010.

As time went on and the value of biodiversity became more appreciated the Department of Agriculture, Fisheries and Food offered a great deal of assistance.

On receipt of the genetic data the Department agreed that the Kerry Bog Pony should be recognised as a breed. For this to happen it was necessary for the Society to have a formal identity with clear Memorandum and Articles of Association. Studbook Rules had to be drawn up with clear procedures for registration and classification. It was decided to become a Friendly Society or Co-operative instead of a Limited Company. Many meetings took place with Department Officials and in time a satisfactory outcome was achieved. Funding was made available from the National Development Plan and from the Department of Agriculture, Fisheries and Food through the Genetic Resources Conservation Trust. The Trust, now known as Genetic Heritage Ireland, is a non-governmental organisation whose main objective is to promote the conservation and sustainable utilisation of Ireland's plant and animal genetic resources. With funding from the Conservation Trust, Aisling Heffernan, a pupil of Dr John Flynn of Weatherbys, undertook a Master's Degree on the "Characterisation of the Kerry Bog Pony".

In 2004, a number of Kerry Bog Ponies were exported to the United States where they are very popular. The American Kerry Bog Pony Society was founded that same year. The American Breed Standard differs from the studbook of origin in the areas of height and colour.

Early members of the Kerry Bog Pony Society

THE KERRY BOG PONY CO-OPERATIVE SOCIETY

The Kerry Bog Pony Co-operative Society came into being in 2005. Later that year the breed was formally recognised by the Department of Agriculture, Fisheries and Food and also the European Union. The Kerry Bog Pony Co-operative Society became the studbook of origin. The Department obtained a derogation from the EU for three years to allow ponies to be taken into the studbook based on phenotype. Horse Sport Ireland maintains the studbook and issues passports on behalf of the Society.

HSI
Horse Sport Ireland is the governing body for equestrian sport in Ireland. It is an umbrella body which represents affiliated equestrian bodies and it incorporates the activities previously governed by the Irish Horse Board and the Equestrian Federation of Ireland.

From 2005-2007 the Kerry Bog Pony Co-operative Society became a partner in the Equisave Programme, a project under Interreg III B, Biodiversity

85

Left: The launch
of the Equisave
project at Kildalton
Agricultural College
in 2006

Right: At the launch
of the first Kerry
Bog Pony brown
passports issued by
Horse Sport Ireland
in 2006

Programme, a European Community initiative, to preserve endangered equine species in the Atlantic areas of Europe. As part of this project seminars on different aspects of conservation took place in France, Spain and Ireland. The Society exhibition stand was present at equine and tourism trade shows such as the RDS Dublin Horse Show, Kildalton equestrian days, Expo Ocio in Madrid and at seminars in Glenbeigh, Co. Kerry.

In 1992 there were 20 known mares and 6 stallions. Today there are over 300 animals in the studbook with 16 distinct stallion lines. The first ponies had been collected in from the hinterland in Kerry. A derogation from the Department of Agriculture Fisheries and Food and the European Union continued this process with ponies of similar characteristics being admitted as Class 1 only. The aim was to gather up all the available local bloodlines before they disappeared in order to achieve as much genetic biodiversity as possible within the breed. Due to these actions Aisling Heffernan found no evidence of a genetic bottleneck in the herd.

The "Black Passports" or information documents were surrendered to the registration department of Horse Sport Ireland and new brown passports were issued in their place. The first Inspections were held for classification within the studbook. These first passports were issued in 2006.

Today the Kerry Bog Pony Co-operative Society can be contacted through their website www.kerrybogpony.ie

INSPECTIONS AND SHOWS

Mary McGrath & Gay Keogh

INSPECTIONS

From 2006-2009 the studbook operated under a derogation whereby animals that met the characteristics of the breed and were identified according to the rules of the studbook were eligible for registration as Class 1 in the studbook. Most of these ponies had no recorded breeding. Live inspections were required to determine compliance with the breed characteristics and these were held in four locations in the first year, Co. Down, Co. Mayo, Co. Kildare and Co. Kerry. In the subsequent years they were held in Kildare and Kerry.

The inspection procedure consisted of a veterinary examination followed by an assessment by two experienced judges for type, conformation and temperament. The inspectors played a crucial role in selecting foundation stock for the Kerry Bog Pony Studbook, based on phenotype. During the three years of the derogation many ponies were brought forward for inspection. In most cases it was necessary to measure and microchip the ponies, take a DNA sample and record the ponies' markings so that passports could be issued. This resulted in long and busy inspection days.

Inspectors played a vital role in selecting suitable ponies for entry into the Studbook under the derogation

Inspections have been held at a number of locations in counties Kerry, Kildare, Mayo and Down

A veterinary surgeon attends the inspections to examine the ponies, record the markings, take hair samples and insert a microchip

The National Show
is an opportunity for
owners to showcase
their ponies and is
the best opportunity
for people to see
ponies of all ages on
display

Nowadays ponies coming in for inspection must already have a passport therefore a lot of this work is already done. These ponies are Class 4, being out of registered parents so based on their results will be reclassified within the studbook. See Chapter 1 – The Kerry Bog Pony Today for Classification details.

SHOWS

The National Show, organised by the Kerry Bog Pony Co-operative Society, is held each year at the Red Fox Inn, Glenbeigh, Co Kerry. Classes are held for young stock and broodmares. A sale of registered ponies is held on the same day. It is an opportunity for breeders to showcase their animals and for onlookers to see many of the best ponies gathered together in one place. It is fitting that this gathering takes place in South West Kerry, the homeland of these distinctive little ponies.

The show takes place in a field beside the Red Fox Inn between the mountains and the bog

THE WORKING LANDSCAPE
OF THE KERRY BOG PONY

John Feehan is a senior lecturer in the Faculty of Agriculture at UCD. He has written extensively on the natural and cultural heritage of the Irish landscape, and on many broader aspects of environmental science. He has won several awards for his work in connection with rural biodiversity and the sustaining of rural community.

Since the early Bronze Age horses were brought to Ireland on many occasions but there is little that can be said to be distinctively Irish about them. All the attention has focused on the Connemara Pony, which is thought to have developed from Arabian horses introduced in the late 18th and during the 19th centuries. However, in 1902 J.C. Ewart, Professor of Natural History

Pony "haunch deep in heather and rushes"

94

at the University of Edinburgh, noted in his article on the Connemara Pony that various other breeds of small horses had '*until recent times been common in the more isolated portions of Great Britain and Ireland*', but as they were on the margins of farming these slipped into undocumented oblivion before their presence had been documented by outside observers.

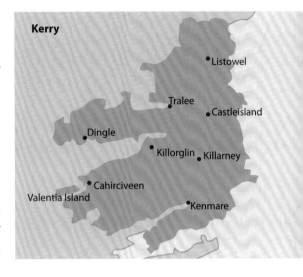

The Kerry Bog Pony is an example of this. Were it not still grazing the hills of the Dingle and Iveragh Peninsulas we might doubt that it had ever existed, just as we deny the existence of other mythical creatures. "What?..... A unique *horse*?..... Haunch-deep in heather and rushes?"

But there it is, where no horse should be, because horses were made for speed and the open, their feed honed by evolution for tip-toed swiftness, their teeth aligned and sharpened for nipping close to the ground the grasses with which they co-evolved. But wherever it came from, the Kerry Bog Pony has made the open hills its own, adapting to this world, so different from the plains for which it is made by nature. As other animals through geological time have dipped their toes into alien elements and become part of them, the bog pony has become an integral part of the hills of south-west Ireland.

As with such horse breeds as the Connemara, Cushendall, Icelandic or Shetland, the Kerry pony probably arose from a blending of an old native breed with later introductions. Exceptional hardiness, endurance, sure-footedness and intelligence are qualities it shares with other moorland and mountain breeds. This is due to the similar pressures and constraints their common environment imposes and a relatively low level of selection pressure for appearance and simple speed. The size of these ponies is another feature they have in common: horses left to fare for themselves on uplands and moors are always of small stature.

The ponies grazed the unenclosed land of the hills, which are dominated by blanket bog, wet heath and heathy grassland. Although this is a very different habitat from the plains, here they found the open space of the ancestral grasslands on which they evolved.

BOG FORMATION

Bogs form in situations where conditions are so wet the ground is permanently waterlogged.

This can come about in two ways. Bogs can develop on the site of lakes or pools that were initially overgrown on their edges by reedmarsh, which was replaced by fen as the area of open water was squeezed out by the accumulating reed peat, and eventually by bog as the thickness of the fen peat left the surface vegetation beyond the reach of groundwater nutrients. Such raised bogs cover large areas of the Irish Midlands where the landscape at the end of the last glacial epoch was dominated by a constellation of lakes in hollows between the ubiquitous moraine, which served as templates for peat formation.

The bogs that dominated the landscape of the western seaboard, and mountain land elsewhere in Ireland, had a different origin. These develop simply because the climate is so wet. Such blanket bog, so called because of the way it envelops the landscape, is found where the rainfall exceeds 1300mm a year.

The boggy hills were not always so. With the return of a warmer climate after the last glacial period they were covered in forest, which was gradually cleared to make way for the fields of Neolithic and Bronze Age farmers – fields where perhaps the ancestors of the Kerry horses grazed. The increased rainfall that characterised the climatic downturn of the Bronze Age caused leaching and erosion of the hill soils, leading to the abandonment of the hill farms and triggering the onset of bog formation.

Turf being gathered in from the bog

Arrival	Date	Name of Period
Man	7000 BC	Stone Age – Hunters (Mesolithic)
Farming	4000 BC	Stone Age – Farmers (Neolithic)
Copper and Tin	2000 BC	Bronze Age
Iron	500 BC	Iron Age
Christianity	400 AD	Early Christian
Normans	1169 AD	Medieval

Development of Blanket Bogs in Ireland

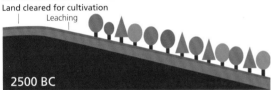

Pine and birch forest

4000 BC

Land cleared for cultivation
Leaching

2500 BC

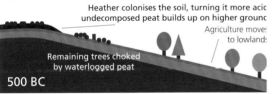

Heather colonises the soil, turning it more acidic
undecomposed peat builds up on higher ground
Agriculture moves to lowlands
Remaining trees choked by waterlogged peat

500 BC

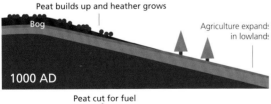

Peat builds up and heather grows
Bog
Agriculture expands in lowlands

1000 AD

Peat cut for fuel
Agriculture

Development of Raised Bogs in Ireland

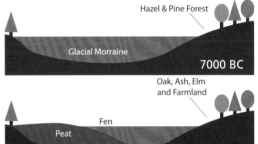

Hazel & Pine Forest
Glacial Morraine
7000 BC

Oak, Ash, Elm and Farmland
Fen
Peat
1500 BC

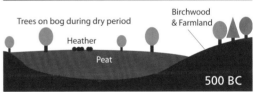

Birchwood & Farmland
Trees on bog during dry period
Heather
Peat
500 BC

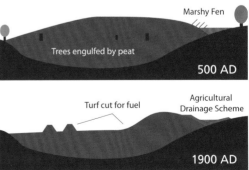

Marshy Fen
Trees engulfed by peat
500 AD

Turf cut for fuel
Agricultural Drainage Scheme
1900 AD

Within the county of
Kerry there are many
different habitats
Photos © Michael
Diggin

A highly varied diet is a major factor in the health and vigour of the ponies, and is not easily achieved under more intensive conditions of cultivation. The grassland on which they generally graze for preference is not the low-diversity sward (consisting largely of ryegrass and clover) to which most horses are confined, but the high-diversity ecosystems of grassy heath, heath and bog with their wide variety of herbs and shrubs that between them provide a far superior balanced diet. And, in the Atlantic climate of the south-west the growing season of this diverse sward extends from one end of the year to the other.

HILLSIDE FORAGE

Although horses are highly efficient grazers, in nature the Kerry Bog Pony's diet is not confined to the grasses that are the standard fare of their more cosseted low-land relatives. During some of the year they show a preference for various kinds of coarse vegetation: heather plants, young furze and an assortment of roots and palatable shoots, to which the great length and strength of the equine jaws are well adapted. This is a matter of instinct in the horse, and is especially evident in hill and moorland ponies when they are replacing their old coats in spring.

Plants:
Top (l-r) Woodrush,
Tormentil, Yarrow
Middle (l-r) Ladies'
Bedstraw, Birdsfoot
Trefoil, Fescue grass
Bottom (l-r):
Bog Pimpernel,
Meadowsweet,
Purple Moor Grass
or Fionán

GRASSLAND FORAGE

Although their work often takes them high into the hills and onto the bogs for which they are named, the ponies graze mainly on the mosaic of grasslands in-between, which provide them with a species-diverse and balanced diet. The main grass species are creeping bent (*Agrostis stolonifera*), Yorkshire fog (*Holcus lanatus*), rough meadow-grass (*Poa trivialis*) and turfed hair-grass (*Deschampsia caespitosa*). Meadow buttercup (*Ranunculus acris*) is widespread, but is avoided by the ponies along with several rush species. Wetter pastures are characterized by species such as silverweed (*Potentilla anserina*), meadowsweet (*Filipendula ulmaria*), water mint (*Mentha aquatica*), marsh bedstraw (*Galium palustre*), lesser spearwort (*Ranunculus flammula*), marsh thistle (*Cirsium palustre*), lady's-smock (*Cardamine pratensis*), yellow iris (*Iris pseudacorus*) and floating sweet-grass (*Glyceria fluitans*).

BIRDS OF THE BOGLANDS

Hen Harrier ♀

Green Plover (Lapwing)

Curlew

Merlin ♀

Heron

Stonechat ♂

Snipe

Meadow pipit

Skylark

Teal ♂

BOGLAND FORAGE

The bog itself is dominated by sedges and the grass known in Kerry as *fionán* (purple moor-grass, *Molinia caerulea*), with an abundance of heather, mosses, lichens and algae and such characteristic species as black bog-rush (*Schoenus nigricans*), devil's-bit scabious (*Succisa pratensis*) and bog pimpernel (*Anagallis tenella*). Where conditions are drier a heathy type of grassland replaces bog, especially where land reclaimed from the hills in pre-Famine times has reverted to rough grazing. These are among the Kerry Bog Pony's favourite pastures. Fescues (*Festuca* species) and bents (*Agrostis*) are the dominant grasses, but every mouthful will contain a bite of such species as yarrow (*Achillea millefolia*), tormentil (*Potentilla erecta*), heath and lady's bedstraws (*Galium* species), bird's-foot trefoil (*Lotus corniculatus* and *L. uliginosus*), heath milkwort (*Polygala serpyllifolia*), common dog violet (*Viola riviniana*), ribwort plantain (*Plantago lanceolata*), bitter vetch (*Lathyrus linifolius*), lousewort (*Pedicularis sylvatica*) and wood-rush (*Luzula* species), each of which makes its unique contribution to a highly-diversified diet.

The complex topography of the countryside supports a rich variety of flora and fauna. Photo © Michael Diggin

Opposite: Birds of the Boglands. Image © Don Conroy

MACHAIR

Closer to the sea the range of the Kerry Bog Pony grades into the coastal grassland known as *machair*, a species-diverse habitat found where coastal sand has been blown inland during stormy weather and subsequently stabilized, providing the foundation for an ecologically important habitat that is found only along parts of the western seaboard of Ireland and Scotland. It is usually an area of flat or undulating plain characterized by unique assemblages of plant and invertebrate species, and is an important habitat for ground-nesting birds. Machair owes much of its distinctiveness to a traditional pattern of regulated communal mixed grazing between March and August, to which ponies contributed. With the breakup of this system over recent decades many areas of machair have become degraded or been reclaimed, and the preservation and restoration of this unique farm habitat is now a matter of considerable concern.

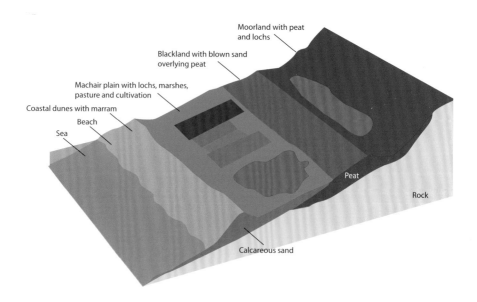

A cross section showing the formation of the costal grassland known as Machair

Opposite: Aerial view of Machair. Photo © Michael Diggin

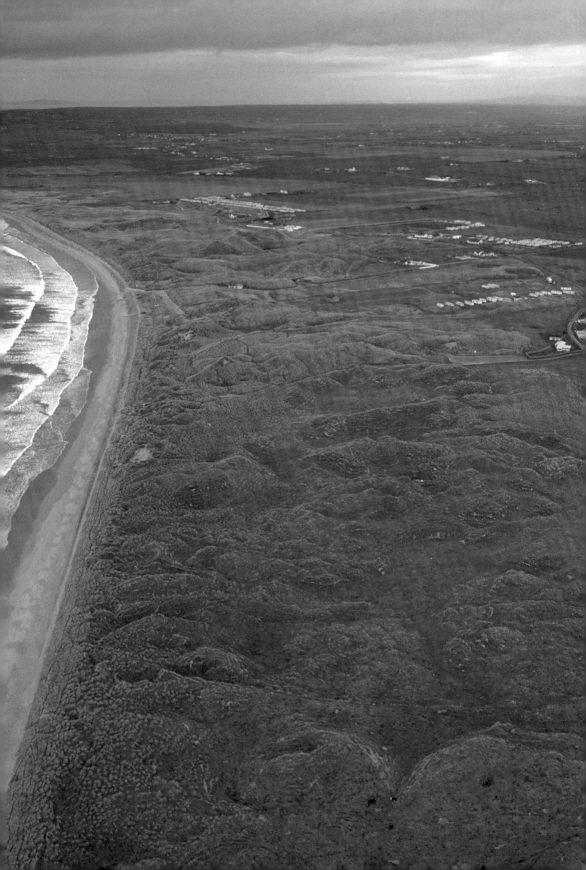

BIODIVERSITY

Mary McGrath & Gay Keogh

What if...

"What if....?"
Thought provoking
image © Annie West

During the first six years of the 21st century, more than 60 breeds of animals – almost one a month – disappeared forever, taking with them their unique genetic make-up. Losing these breeds is like losing a global insurance policy against future threats to food security. It undermines capacity to adapt livestock populations to environmental changes, emerging diseases or changing consumer demands.

WHAT IS BIODIVERSITY?

The amazing variety of life on Earth is called  biodiversity. Every living thing has a place in the ecosystem and should be protected to preserve the balance of nature. All natural things including humans are interdependent. Modern practices are threatening to destroy species' richness and we have no way of knowing how this will affect our own survival in the long term.

A TIME FOR ACTION

The United Nations declared 2010 to be the International Year of Biodiversity, in order to celebrate life on Earth and the value of biodiversity for our lives and invited the world to take action to safeguard the variety of life on Earth.

We have no idea what the future may hold. Focusing on one trait to the exclusion of all others can cause major problems in a breed. For example, fertility and hardiness can suffer in the search for milk production in cows. There are a very high percentage of Caesarean sections in some beef breeds due to calving difficulties caused by attempts to produce the biggest calf possible. By breeding for specific traits we have no idea what other aspects of the breed we affect. In 1975 studies were carried out by Belyaev & Trut on Siberian foxes in the fur trade. When these foxes were bred selectively for tameness this had the completely unanticipated result of changing their coat colour.

Recent years have seen substantial erosion of genetic diversity. In the 20th century livestock development concentrated on a very small number of breeds worldwide, frequently without due consideration to the way in which production environments affect animals' ability to survive, produce and reproduce. Many indigenous breeds, some of which are threatened with extinction, have characteristics such as resilience to climatic stress and resistance to diseases and parasites, which make them well adapted to local conditions, and which are of great potential importance to future livestock production. The hardiness of native breeds is a trait that may become more valuable in the fight against new and mutating viral infections. Consequently, it makes good sense to preserve as large a gene pool as possible as a safeguard for the future as we have no way of knowing when it will be needed.

The Kerry Cow is a hardy, productive, long living breed particularly well adapted to its environment

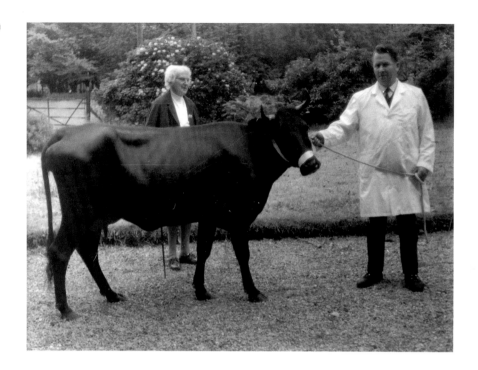

F.A.O.

In 2007, the Food and Agricultural Organisation of the United Nations – F.A.O., unveiled The State of the World's Animal Genetic Resources for Food and Agriculture, a first-ever, global assessment of the status and trends of animal genetic resources. This work serves as an authoritative reference from which to plan management projects. Of the 7,600 breeds reported to F.A.O. by its Member Countries, more than 1,500 are at risk of extinction or are already extinct.

THE KERRY BOG PONY

The story of the Kerry Bog Pony illustrates the classic history of a local breed in danger of extinction. It was originally imported by people who had a need for such an animal. We do not know much about how the pony was used or what it originally looked like only that it must have had a definite purpose. These early settlers used selective breeding to pass on desirable traits

while omitting the undesirable ones. For centuries the pony continued to have a meaningful role in the life of the South Kerry area. However major changes in land use and transport meant that the function of the Kerry Bog Pony was gradually eroded until during the latter part of the 20th century it no longer had a role to play. Ireland had become a member of the European Union. Methods of farming and the profile of those farming the land also changed. Land use was maximised and marginal land was drained and reclaimed. Sheep grazed the less productive land subsidised by grant aid. Small ponies were only kept by very few traditional farmers. Their numbers declined until they had almost become extinct.

Opposite: Cultivation ridges or "lazy beds" mark the endeavours of past generations. Photo © Michael Diggin

POTATO BLIGHT

The Great Famine of 1845-1849, was the result of relying on only one potato variety. Since new potato plants do not come as a result of reproduction but rather from pieces of the parent plant, no genetic diversity is developed, and as the entire crop is essentially a clone of one potato, it is especially susceptible to an epidemic. In the 1840s, much of Ireland's population depended on potatoes for food. They planted a variety of potato called the "Lumper", which was susceptible to a rot-causing plasmodiophorid called *Phytophthora infestans*. This blight destroyed the vast majority of the potato crop, leaving one million people to starve to death while another million emigrated.

In a constantly changing world dependence on so few plants and animals makes us very vulnerable to crop and livestock diseases and the effects of climate change. Fourteen animal species account for 90% of the livestock we raise and about 30 crop species supply 90% of the calories in our diet. This is a tiny slice of the 1.5 million known plant and animal species.

PRESERVATION OF THE KERRY BOG PONY

Under the National Development Plan the breeding of rare and endangered breeds is encouraged. The Kerry Bog Pony Co-operative Society has undertaken a number of conservation initiatives in conjunction with the Department of Agriculture, Fisheries and Food.

Kerry Bog Ponies survived in small numbers until the 1990s

Concerned breeders had ensured the survival of the Kerry Bog Pony, albeit in small numbers until the 1990s. However, the ponies were not yet formally recognised as a breed. In order to establish a clear identity for the endangered breed the first step was to define exactly what a Kerry Bog Pony was. In 1994 Weatherbys DNA Laboratory began to carry out blood typing and gene frequency studies on identified genetic markers in the Kerry Bog Pony population.

"There is adequate evidence (from these gene frequency calculations) to show that this population has significant difference in genetic frequency values to consider the pony to be a particular breed in its own right".(Dr John Flynn, Weatherbys DNA Laboratory, 1995.

One surprising result of this study was the fact that despite co-existing on the Western seaboard for generations the genetic frequency values in the Kerry Bog Pony significantly differ from the Connemara Pony.

In 2005 the Department of Agriculture, Fisheries and Food formally recognised the breed thanks to the Weatherbys DNA analysis and John Mulvihills pedigree records. Studbook rules were drawn up. While the studbook was in a foundation period many animals did not have pedigree information recorded. Consequently, from 2006 to 2009, the studbook operated under a derogation whereby animals that met the characteristics of the breed and were identified according to the rules were eligible for registration as Class 1 in the studbook. Live inspections were required to determine compliance with the breed characteristics. This derogation, which was authorised by the Department of Agriculture, Fisheries and Food operated for three years until the 31st of December 2009. After this date, the studbook was closed and the Society may decide to open a Supplementary Section to infuse new genes into the population at a future date if they so wish. However, at present there is no evidence of a genetic bottleneck in the Kerry Bog Pony population.

As a further aid to breeders the Department employed the Irish Cattle Breeders Federation to carry out an inbreeding analysis of the ponies registered in the studbook. Letters were sent to each breeder outlining the inbreeding coefficient of their individual mares and the stallions on the approved register.

The new rules required that ponies be brought forward for inspection

While the herd numbers are still not large, at present there is sufficient genetic diversity to avoid inbreeding. Currently there are 277 females and 121 males (colts, geldings and stallions) registered in the studbook. There are 16 distinct stallion lines. Careful selection will minimise the danger of inbreeding with all its resulting problems.

EQUISAVE 2005–2007

Equisave was a European biodiversity programme for the preservation of endangered equine breeds in the Atlantic regions of Europe. The Kerry Bog Pony Co-operative Society participated in this scheme "To Preserve and Promote the Kerry Bog Pony with special reference to Conservation, Environment and Tourism in Ireland" with our Equisave partners in France, Spain and Portugal. This illustrated the problems encountered by localised equine breeds and highlighted their plight in a European context.

REPS

The Rural Environment Protection Scheme, funded by the National Development Plan, contains a Supplementary Measure which is intended to promote the conservation of Animal Genetic Resources (Rare Breeds). It recognises that local animal breeds play a significant role in maintaining the rural environment and represent a significant element of the cultural heritage of farming in Ireland. In 2006 the Kerry Bog Pony became one of the breeds eligible for an annual payment.

RARE BREED FESTIVALS

In 2006, with funding from the Department, the Kerry Bog Pony Co-operative Society organised a small rare breed festival and seminar at Muckross Traditional Farms, Muckross House, Killarney.

The following year a much larger festival was held in conjunction with Iverk Show, Piltown, Ireland's oldest agricultural show, which brought together many rare breeds including all of the animals eligible for REPS supplementary payments. The objective was to place the Kerry Bog Pony in context while raising awareness of endangered species.

Rare breed festivals celebrate the survival of our native breeds and highlight those that are under threat today

Kerry Bog Ponies are used in Birdwatch Ireland reserves to manage the grassland habitat

Breeders are the backbone of the Society and the future lies in their hands

CONSERVATION GRAZING

Kerry Bog Ponies also benefit the ecological balance of the countryside. Birdwatch Ireland, the national organisation for the protection of birds, has purchased several geldings to graze their reserves. Unlike cattle and sheep, the ponies are selective grazers and leave tufts of grass and ungrazed areas which are ideal for nesting birds.

BREEDERS

The crucial role of local farmers as custodians of the breed must be acknowledged. Traditional livestock keepers are skilled breeders and as a rule they are small-scale farmers running the farm as a family enterprise. The breeders must be active partners in any ongoing conservation programme. The best plan for success should combine traditional knowledge with modern science-based practices.

The identification of the Kerry Bog Pony as an individual breed adds to the number of Ireland's equine breeds. Re-establishing a disappearing breed in the 21st century is an important achievement for Ireland's biodiversity programme.

CRAFTS AND PRACTICES ASSOCIATED WITH THE KERRY BOG PONY

David Shaw-Smith D.litt (h.c. Dublin) Aos is an independent documentary film maker based in Co. Mayo. His films on traditional Irish crafts, including the highly acclaimed series 'Hands' and over 100 other documentaries, have been seen all over the world and have won him many awards. He is the author of 'Traditional Crafts of Ireland'.

Raw materials for ponies' harness and creels were grown on the small holdings

I remember my father telling me that he and my grandfather saw a strange sight when on a fishing holiday in Kerry many years ago. They rounded a bend in the road and saw in the distance a man walking away from them

118

The harness was made from hay or straw and the creels from willow "Sallies"

wearing a long raincoat and what appeared to be high-heels, making short little steps. As they came closer the puzzle was solved: it was a big man, riding a very small pony, his feet trailing the ground, his frieze coat thrown over the pony's rump – their first encounter with the Kerry Bog Pony! More than a half-century later I was to meet the pony – nose to nose so to speak…. that's not to say we were of equal height!

In earliest times after its introduction to Co. Kerry, before roads were built, the pony was used as a pack animal because of its unusual stamina and strength: walking in trains across uneven ground and negotiating narrow mountain passes, carrying loads over its back in sacks and creels of all descriptions.

Local craftsmen depended on the pony to make a living. The basket maker made creels from willow and hazel rods. (Woven creels and saddle-mats were often made on the home farm from both Sally Willow (saileach) and woven and twisted straw or hay (sugán). In the 19th century it is documented that harness was made from straw.) The pony required shoes that involved the blacksmith who also shod cartwheels and the cartwright to build Flat-Carts or *Cars,* and Traps and maybe a *Slype* or two; a low toboggan-

The evolution
of horse drawn
vehicles paralleled
the development
of the road system.
Lower right photo ©
macmonagle.com

© macmonagle.com

120

like slide-car with iron-shod runners used to draw turf (peat) off the bog where a wheeled vehicle could become mired.

Left: Bank of turf showing marks of "slane" cuts. Photo © Michael Diggin

The turf was cut from the turf-bank with a '*Slane*', a special long-headed spade with a combined narrow, right-angled side that supported and held the sod in place when thrown back over the shoulder onto the ground behind the turf-cutter, where it was later built into small pyramids of turf to dry. Later it was stacked in '*Ricks*' alongside the narrow bog roads. When fully dried at the end of August and into September it was drawn to the homestead or farm in flat-carts that had detachable sides to enable the load to be increased. Once there, the turf was re-stacked and covered with rushes or reeds to keep the rain out. Turf could then be removed from one end for the open fire or range and the stack recovered. For myself the aromatic smell of smoke from the open turf fire brings back happy memories of my teenage years living in Baurisheen on Lough Corrib near Oughterard in Co. Galway – Connemara Pony country!

Right: A rick of turf by the side of the road. Photo © Michael Diggin

The blacksmith was often referred to as '*The King of Crafts*'. In earlier times the blacksmith made weaponry such as '*Pikes*', a long-handled type of spear or lance, some combined with a right-angled, downward-facing curved blade that allowed pike-men on foot to sever the reins of a mounted horseman. The blacksmith was also renowned throughout Ireland for making and supplying many of the other craftsmen with the tools of their trade, and additional '*bibs and bobs*' for the harness-maker, saddler and collar-maker. Further trades were indirectly involved such as the miller to roll and crush the pony's oats in wintertime.

Sallies (Irish Saileach) were grown by small holders to provide their own raw materials. Photo © David Shaw-Smith

Opposite: The stages of making a creel. Photos © David Shaw-Smith

On Sundays the pony might be required to bring the family to Mass in the tub-trap (a task taken over elsewhere in Ireland by the famous Irish Draught horse) and on weekdays to draw milk to the local creamery. On fair-days it would transport farm-produce for sale to the nearest town or village in the flat-cart. The driver on returning home, most likely fortified with a few pints of Guinness, would be standing upright, tearing along with one foot forward to balance himself as he held the reins.

Back in the early 1970s there was a cartwright in Caherciveen, Co. Kerry. Frequently, when driving through the village I would see his small, beautifully-made carts out in the street for sale. If my memory serves me right the body was painted a pale powder-blue colour and the other parts were offset in a bright 'Cart Orange' (hence the local name for the paint.)

Most homesteads in the Irish countryside had a 'Sally Garden' where different varieties of willows grew and if you couldn't weave your own baskets (as many did) the local Basket maker certainly could! Creels were made in various shapes and sizes from a back creel that a man might carry to separately paired creels for a donkey or Kerry Bog Pony. Strong tall Sally rods were driven into the ground forming the rectangular shape of an upturned creel and weaving began from the eventual mouth upwards. When the creel reached

123

Sugán rope was made by twisting long stems of grass or straw with a special tool in a process called "ag casadh an tsugán". This rope could then be used for many purposes including making harness or chair seats. Photos © David Shaw-Smith

Those who could afford to used leather collars made by the local harness maker. Photo © David Shaw-Smith

the correct height the willow was crossed over to form a skeleton base and interwoven. The creel was then pulled out of the ground to complete the rim.

In the days when the horse was 'King of the Road' there were many carriage-builders in Ireland. Colm and his brother Kevin Breen in Enniscorthy, Co. Wexford were possibly the last of the old traditional carriage-builders. Their carriage-works listed five distinct and separate trades under the same roof. Kevin and his assistant were the carpenters and carriage body-builders, doubling as wood turners when making a 'Spindle Gig'. Their wheelwright made a wide variety of wheels for the various horse-drawn vehicles. The blacksmith and his assistant forged all the metal parts and shod the wheels. The carriage works also made Traps, Horse Cabs and Dogcarts, Floats and Landaus. Colm Breen was 'the painter' who painted and lined the wheels and decorated the other body parts, while finally the upholsterer fitted out the interiors. In rural

There was always work for the harness maker when horses and ponies were in everyday use. Photo © David Shaw-Smith

Ireland the situation was quite different. The local cartwright was capable of turning his hand to making all the wooden parts of a cart including the wheels and the blacksmith shod them – though the cartwright may well have done that job as well!

Having recently seen the Kerry Bog Pony in its 'homeland', I now have one remaining ambition: to ride the pony up the beautiful Glen that rises above Caragh Lake near Glenbeigh in South West Kerry. And by the way, when you finally get to see the pony, it won't be wearing high-heels!

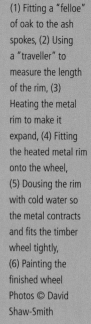

(1) Fitting a "felloe" of oak to the ash spokes, (2) Using a "traveller" to measure the length of the rim, (3) Heating the metal rim to make it expand, (4) Fitting the heated metal rim onto the wheel, (5) Dousing the rim with cold water so the metal contracts and fits the timber wheel tightly, (6) Painting the finished wheel
Photos © David Shaw-Smith

WHAT DOES THE FUTURE HOLD?

Mary McGrath & Gay Keogh

One of the objectives of The Kerry Bog Pony Co-operative Society is to preserve the pony in its place of origin. This means finding a meaningful role for the pony in south Kerry.

Kerry is unique in having the most amazing landscape of mountains, lakes, rivers and boglands. Its extensive coastline ranges from towering cliffs to long sandy beaches. The Lakes of Killarney and the Gap of Dunloe have attracted tourists for over 300 years. Some of these early visitors kept journals of their travels which have survived to this day. Elsewhere in this book we have quoted their descriptions of encounters with the native Kerry pony.

Kerry's natural beauty attracts many visitors every year

Photos © Michael Diggan

WHAT IS ECOTOURISM?

Ecotourism is a form of tourism to undisturbed areas high in natural beauty or biodiversity that strives to minimize ecological impact or damage.

Recent surveys have shown that visitors' main reasons for coming to Ireland include beautiful scenery, friendly hospitable people, safe and secure destinations, natural unspoilt environment, the easy and relaxed pace of life, good range of natural attractions, interesting history and culture and a country suitable for touring. Kerry offers all of this and more. In the past year over 1.1 million domestic visitors and 1.5 million overseas tourists visited the south west of Ireland. The opportunity to introduce some of these visitors to our "small native pony" is too good to ignore. Local and national authorities have been approached to gauge the level of interest in this area.

ECOTOURISM

Recent Fáilte Ireland research in our overseas markets has shown that the demand for high-quality ecotourism experiences in Ireland is on the rise. Increasingly, people are looking not just to escape on their holidays, but to have new experiences and in particular to engage with nature and learn something new. 'Ecotourism', 'green tourism' and 'responsible tourism' are all phrases that have entered the tourism

The Kerry Bog
Village is a popular
tourist attraction in
Glenbeigh, Co. Kerry

Opposite: Drawings
by children at
Curraheen National
School. Teacher:
Helen Murphy
(1) Amber Shresta
Age 11, (2) Jessica
Carroll Age 13,
(3) Cathriona
Walsh Age 9,
(4) Aran Mulvihill
Age 9, (5) Darren
McGillycuddy
Age11, (6) Emer
Moore Age 11

*vocabulary over the past few years and they reflect the changing tastes of our visi-
tors. In order for tourism in Ireland to respond effectively to these new trends, we
must ensure that we can deliver high-quality and sustainable experiences for the
visitor. Projects involving the conservation of a rare or endangered species provide
opportunities for tourism to 'give something back' by actually aiding the conservation cause and enriching the visitor experience at the same time. The 'rediscovery' of
the Kerry Bog Pony is a great story — for both ourselves and our visitors. It is a
story rich in local distinctiveness and yet provides links to other parts of the world
through the DNA research that has been undertaken. It also provides opportunities
for tourism to raise awareness of the pony among our visitors and to explore how
we could develop visitor experiences in Kerry which could bring people 'up close and
personal' with the ponies, ensuring that sustainability and conservation are kept to
the fore. This is a great story for Kerry and a great story for tourism.*
(Paddy Mathews, Environment and Planning, Fáilte Ireland).

Currently there are two main tourist attractions where Kerry Bog Ponies can
be seen: Muckross Traditional Farms, Killarney where Toddy Doyle has provided great support and the Kerry Bog Village at the Red Fox Inn, Glenbeigh.
These are extremely popular with visitors who see the ponies as a symbol of
the unique rural heritage of Kerry. It is an opportunity for young visitors to
see and experience a way of life, familiar to their parents and grandparents,

1

2

3

4

THE BOG PONY

5

6

Newborn Kerry
Bog Pony foal on
display at Muckross
Traditional Farms,
Killarney. Photo
Valerie O'Sullivan
Photographer/
Muckross House
Archive

which has disappeared today. Milk was brought to the creamery, turf was brought home from the bog and hay was brought in from the meadow. These are images linked in our minds with Ireland of times past. There is a need to highlight and optimise these memories and show that they should be valued in today's fast-paced world.

The tourists already come to Kerry, the ponies exist in Kerry, the bogs are widespread. The opportunities that this combination of assets offers are waiting to be exploited. The best form of conservation lies in finding a viable role for the ponies in their own landscape. In France, Spain and Portugal a new tourism venture has become very popular. It involves the use of ponies as pack animals on walking tours. Each walker is assigned their own pony which can carry their rucksacks and their lunch, as well as tired children when necessary. The interaction with the pony adds immeasurably to the enjoyment of the occasion.

The isolation, the climate and the range of habitats in Kerry have resulted in a species-rich environment. Kerry is the last surviving refuge for many rare

species such as the Natterjack Toad, the Kerry Lily and the Red Deer to name but a few. More and more people are coming to appreciate the importance of biodiversity and it is a growing reason why visitors travel to Kerry. This is another area where the Kerry Bog Pony can play an important role.

"Throwing the turf." Many traditional farm and country activities have disappeared within living memory. Photo © Macmonagle.com

BIODIVERSITY

Ireland as a whole with its location at the far western edge of Europe has a significant role to play in European Biodiversity and indeed World Biodiversity. Within Ireland the counties on the western seaboard have an even greater role to play. Geography and politics at regional and local level have given the land and species dependent upon it breathing space or more accurately survival space. In many other areas intensive agriculture and industrialisation have played a significant part in altering the landscape and altering its biodiversity potential.

A recent study by the Kerry County Council Heritage Office identified almost 60 non-domesticated plant and animal species of national or international significance

While building up the breeding herd is very important for the development of the breed, it is also desirable that people realise how suitable the Kerry Bog Pony is as a versatile performing pony

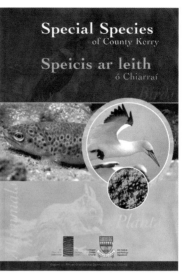

with distribution patterns limited to within the county. A DNA study of certain fish species identified county specific strains of Arctic Char and Trout. The work on the Arctic Char brings into question many theories in relation to glaciation and animal migration and their effects on the flora and fauna of the county. A number of 'special species' identified are, it would appear, extinct.

The story of the Kerry Bog Pony shows us what can be done by relatively few individuals to bring a species back from the brink of extinction, preventing the further degradation of our biodiversity reserve. The Kerry Bog Pony is an important piece of our cultural heritage having played significant roles in agriculture and tourism. The pony has been bred to be ideally suited to the county's diverse terrain. There are many plants and animals known, and I'm sure awaiting discovery, which survive only in the unique climate and topography of County Kerry. Once these special species are eliminated from our biodiversity reserve they cannot be re-introduced and we will be all the poorer for it. One can only hope that these flora and fauna can also be championed by groups like the Kerry Bog Pony Co-operative Society and these groups will be given assistance to protect and preserve our biodiversity, culture and heritage.

(Una Cosgrove, Heritage Officer, Kerry County Council).

While the risk of extinction has receded, the Kerry Bog Pony can only thrive as an active population with a real purpose.

The environment of Kerry supports many unique species

The role of the owners and breeders is very important in preserving and promoting this special pony

These ponies can participate in all equestrian disciplines and active participation will ensure that more people get to know and appreciate our third native breed. However, the Kerry Bog Pony is a small, hardy, working pony; it is not a pretty show pony. It is sound, has a good temperament and is healthy and strong. All these characteristics are the result of generations of breeding for a specific purpose in a specific locality. Today, the responsibility lies with the breeders to preserve these unique traits. There is always a temptation to change aspects of a breed to make it prettier or more commercial. Now is the time to create a role for these ponies as they are and not allow them to change into a generic show pony. Currently, there are few opportunities to showcase the Kerry Bog Pony. There is a need for action, both in developing suitable classes and activities and in supporting them.

The Kerry Bog Pony Co-operative Society has in the past organised successful education days and seminars. It is one of the stated objectives of the Society to continue to arrange suitable training courses to promote the best interests of the pony.

The DNA analysis of the breed has placed the Kerry Bog Pony in a worldwide context. Its unique genetic makeup is of considerable interest to the greater scientific community. If you own a Kerry Bog Pony you own one of the rarest breeds of pony or horse in Europe. With this comes the responsibility to participate in the preservation and survival of this rare and ancient breed.

Photo © Pascal Lando

FURTHER READING

BOOKS

An Oxonian with illustrations by John Leech, *A Little Tour in Ireland being a Visit to Dublin, Galway, Connemara, Killarney etc.* London Bradbury Agnew & Co 1859

Arts, Culture and Heritage Department, Kerry County Council, *Special Species of County Kerry*. No publication date.

Bell, Jonathon & Watson, Mervyn, *A history of Irish Farming 1750-1950*, Four Courts Press, 2008

Clutton-Brock, Juliet, *A Natural History of Domesticated Mammals*, Cambridge University Press , 1987

Cox, Michael F., *Notes of the History of the Irish Horse*, Sealy, Bryers and Walker, Congested District Board, Dublin, 1897

Coyne, William P. Ed., *The Irish horse-breeding industry: Ireland, Agricultural and Industrial.* Revised and enlarged from the edition of 1901, issued as an official handbook for the Irish pavilion, Glasgow International Exhibition, Brown and Nolan, Dublin, 1901

Coyne, William P., Ed., *Statistical survey of Irish agriculture: Ireland, Agricultural and Industrial,* Department of Agriculture and Technical Instruction for Ireland, Browne and Nolan, Dublin, 1902

Crowley, John & Sheehan, John Eds, *The Iveragh Peninsula*, Cork University Press, 2009

Dickson, David *Old World Colony – Cork and South Munster 1630-1830.* Cork University Press, 2005.

Draper, Judith, *Horse Breeds of the World*, Anness Publishing Ltd, London, 1996

Estyn Evans, E., *Irish Folk Ways*, Routledge & Kegan Paul, 1957

Estyn Evans, E., *The Personality of Ireland – Habitat, Heritage and History*, The Lilliput Press, 1992

Ewart J.C. (1902). The Ponies of Connemara. In William P. Coyne (ed.), *Ireland Agricultural and Industrial,* pp. 332-358. Brown and Nolan, Dublin, 1902

Hartley Edwards, Elwyn. *The Encyclopedia of the Horse*, Dorling Kindersley, London, 1994

Heffernan, Aisling, *Characterisation of the Kerry Bog Pony*, Master's Thesis, NUI Dublin 2007

Kavanagh, Rhoda, 'The Horse in Viking Ireland', Bradley, John Ed. *Settlement and Society in Medieval Ireland.* Boethius Press, Kilkenny, 1988

Kelly, Fergus, *Early Irish Farming*, Dublin Institute for Advanced Studies, 2000

Kennedy, Liam & Solar, Peter M. *Irish Agriculture – A Price History*, Royal Irish Academy, 2007

Lewis, Colin, *Horse Breeding in Ireland*, JA Allen, London, 1980

MacCana, Proinsias, *Celtic Mythology*, Hamlyn Publishing Group, London 1970

McCormick, Finbar & Murray, Emily, *Knowth and the Zooarcheology of Early Christian Ireland*, Royal Irish Academy, 2007

McGrath, Mary & Griffith, Joan, *The Irish Draught Horse*, Collins Press, Cork, 2005

O'Cleirigh, Nellie, *Valentia. A Different Irish Island.* Portobello Press, Dublin, 1992

O'Siodhacháin Donal Ed. *Beara to Breifne.* Cló Dunaire / Irish & Celtic Publications, Cork ,1987

Pickeral, Tansin, *The Encyclopedia of Horses and Ponies*, Parragon, Bath, 1999

Pilcher, Jonathon & Hall, Valerie, Flora Hibernica, The Collins Press, 2001

Quale, Thomas, *General View of the Agriculture of the Isle of Man,* W. Bulmer & Co Cleveland Row, London, 1812

Rastall, R.H., *Agricultural Geology* , Cambridge University Press, 1916

Redcliffe N.Salaman, *The History and Social Influence of the Potato,* Cambridge University Press, 1949

Reidy, Mary Denis, *Breaking the Silence*, M&R Publishing, Glenbeigh, Co Kerry, 2004

Returns of Agricultural Produce Census,1841

Shaw-Smith, David, *Irish Traditional Crafts*, Thames and Hudson, London, 1984

Shaw-Smith, David, *Traditional Crafts of Ireland*, Thames & Hudson, London, 2003

Wollaston Hutton, A. Ed., *Arthur Young's Tour in Ireland (1776-1779)*, Arthur G.Bell and Sons 1892

TECHNICAL JOURNALS

Ewart, J. C. *"The tarpan and its relationship with wild and domestic horses"*. *Nature* **74**: 113-115 (1906).

Davenport, D.P., Sleeman J.L., & Woodman P.C, Ed.: *Mind the Gap – Postglacial colonization of Ireland.* The Irish Naturalists' Journal 2008

McGahern, A.M.Edwards, C.J., Bower, M.A., Heffernan, A.,Park, S.D.E., Brophy, P.O., Bradley,D.G., MacHugh,D.E., and Hill, E.W., *Mitochondrial DNA sequence diversity in extant Irish horse populations and in ancient horses*, Animal Genetics, Volume 37, Issue 5, pages 498-502 Published online 1st September 2006.

SELECTED MAGAZINE ARTICLES

Cheval Magazine, July 2006, Text: Pierre-Brice Lebrun/ ABCD'AIR, Photos: Alen Meaulle/ABCD'AIR "L'Irlande, l'autre pays du cheval"

Freizeit im Sattel , Bonn, Germany, 1 January 1997, Article

Ireland of the Welcomes, September-October 1995, Article Vol. 44 No.5

Ireland of the Welcomes, November-December 2005, "The Kerry Bog Pony, Irish Donkey and the Irish Draught Horse", Vol. 54, No. 6.

Ireland's Equestrian, Date, Front page plus article

Peatland News, Autumn 2004, Front page and article

Pegasus , Lindau, Germany, May 2005, Front page and article

Nag Mag, Feb 2007, Front page and Article

Sabots, No14 September 2006, Texte & Photos: Emmanuelle Poiret, "Le Kerry Bog Pony – Le Diamond Brut de l'Irlande"

The Native Pony, July 2006, Front page and Article

SELECTED NEWSPAPER ARTICLES AND PHOTOGRAPHS

Farming Independent, 23rd March 2004, Anne Lucey, "Kerry Bog Pony clear favourite in Ohio"

Farming Independent, 8th February 2006, Anne-Marie Walsh, "Heard the one about passports for ponies?"

Ireland's Horse Review, 2001, Photo, Bog Birch, Champion IPS Show, Thomastown,

Ireland's Horse Review, May 2003, "Recognition of Kerry Bog Ponies"

Ireland's Horse Review, August 2006, Liam O'Mochain, "Kerry Bog Pony Society"

Irish Farmers' Journal, 9th March 2002, Quentin Doran-O'Reilly, "Kerry Bog Pony is saved from Extinction"

Irish Farmers' Journal, 15th April 2006, Catherine Keena, "Kerry Bog Pony"

Irish Farmers' Journal, 23rd March 2004, Catherine Keena, "Festival of Rare Breeds"

Irish Independent, 23rd March 2004, Page 8, Photo John Mulvihill and Flashy Fox report on Columbus Ohio

Irish Examiner, 3rd March 1998, Front page, MacMonagle photograph

Irish Examiner, 9th March 2009, "New Era for Kerry Bog Pony"

Kerry Bog Pony News, 2005-2007, "The Kerry Bog Pony Co-operative Society"

Kerry's Eye 17 February 1994, Russell McMorran, Front page, "Kerry Pones Best in Ireland"

Kerryman, 8th April 2004, "The Workhorse of the Bogs"

Kerryman, 2nd June 2010, Valerie O'Sullivan/Gemma Kavanagh, "Buttercup, our new Bog Pony"

Kilkenny People, 1999, Agricultural Review, Front page and article

The European 3-9 June 1994, No 212 Miriam Lord, Front page, "Race is on to Save Bog Pony", Photo and Article

The Kingdom, 5th August 2004, "Kerry Bog Pony gets Hero Status at launch of Mary's Labour of Love"

The Kingdom, 28th April 2005, "New project aims to save Kerry Bog Pony"

The Kingdom, 9th January 2006, "It's cover pin-up treatment for stylish Kerry Bog Pony"

The Irish Times, 24th March 1995, Seán MacConnell, "Plan to save rare pony"

The Irish Times, 6th October 2007, Front page photo and article, John and Rae Brocklehurst with Flashy Fox

The Irish Times, 8th February 2006, Seán MacConnell, "Kerry Bog Pony given official status as rare breed", Photo and article

The Kingdom, 30th October 2007, Photo. John Mulvihill at Show

The Kerryman, 11th February, 1994, Front page photo and article, Joe Walsh and John O'Donohue

The Kerryman, October 21st 1994, Front page photo and article "Ponies to North of Ireland", Eugene McGovern, Hugh O'Kane and Gerry McFarland, Omagh

The Kerryman, 5th August 2004, Launch of *Breaking the Silence*, Mary Denis Reidy, Caragh Bridge Brendan Kennelly Foreword

TELEVISION PROGRAMMES

Bazal Productions Ltd Channel 4

Bgs productions for Tommy Scott Video

Nationwide

Kenny Live

Ear to the Ground

TV3 Evening News - Passport launch 2006

WEBSITE

www.kerrybogpony.ie

INDEX

About the authors

Mary McGrath and Gay Keogh are sisters and were raised in a horse-loving environment at The Curragh, Co. Kildare.

Mary, an art conservator, has worked in Harvard and Denver Universities and the Getty Museum in the United States. Here in Ireland, she has provided consultancy services to the Hugh Lane Gallery and the Irish Museum of Modern Art, as well as many of the leading art collections in the country. She set up the Irish Horse Museum in Kildare. At home as well as her Kerry Bog Ponies, Mary also keeps Irish Draughts, Connemaras and Irish Glen of Imaal Terriers. Previous publications include *The Irish Draught Horse — A History.*

Gay has a great interest in the environment and lives with her husband Joe on a farm bordering a river which is a haven for wildlife. She has studied Archaeology, English and Equine Science and has worked for twelve years in marketing. Gay breeds Irish Draught Horses and Kerry Bog Ponies and also has Irish Glen of Imaal Terriers.